aturn

Preface:

   Imagination in itself is not necessary bad, evil, or negative, but sometimes helps wield the constructive creating force in man to make the progress of science, technology, literature and poetry and social justice possible, just to name a few. To make a more beautiful world come alive! To make progress here on earth! "Some see things as they are and say "why?" But I saw things that never were and said why not...!" (Robert Kennedy)   And after all "it is the quality of imagination before actualization"! (Paul Johnson) Things were in many cases thought into being before they came into being! Think about the people that jumped off high places with home-made wings on, or those that made gliders to fly high whether it worked for them or not. Think about the Wright brothers at Kitty Hawk who dreamed of making the first manned airplane that was run by a gas turbine engine! Then it happened! And what about more modern times- Kurt Vonegut writing about a society with any number of technological advancements for man in space being possible way before they happened that apparently came out of his imagination itself sometimes......! Now they are a reality! Then too think About Ronald

aturn

Regan who dreamed of getting Russia to pledge democracy and knocking down the Iron Curtain and look what happened in his second term- both of these by the hand of God I believe!

To dream a dream of possibility for man before it happens that includes imagination that precedes greatness in science, technology, and literature that then comes along! Martin Luther King, fighter for equal- rights dreamed of the possibility for social justice in America for all where it turned out to be possible instead of impossible. "Halllelujiah!" To be the drafter of the Declaration of Independence Thomas Jefferson who envisioned a government with individual rights for its citizens which included no doubt helping make the signing of the bill of rights in the constitution happen! "Hallelujiah!"

I believe it really takes being a visionary for science or technology or the rights of man before they come about. I remember a speech where Jesse Jackson told the next generation, " to not give up their dreams.." This speech inspired me to keep on truckin with my education and what I have to share with others on mental illness instead of not shine my light!

aturn

Finally I remember when I was twenty-two yrs. old that I went to a Holly Roller meeting one evening with an evangelist named T.L. Osborne speaking. His sermon that night turned out to be the greatest inspiration of my life. He looked right at me at one point during his sermon and said "Love others than you'll have the victory!" I knew that this was just what I needed to hear that night! I was having a struggle in the new department at work getting along with some employees that worked in it longer than me. They were so mean to me....but after I went to this HR meeting this night I became a changed person that could now get along much better with everybody, and more confident in myself! I had already visualized myself a winner with more love inside for others that could also express it in everyday life too! Now I could do this! I became no respecter of person trying to reach all with every day communication including work related and being a friend in that regard. I now entered a higher love inside by God that guided me to be no respecter of person but love everyone with a Big love! My personality grew like much faster with this bigger Love inside that was more far reaching! It is the Big leap of faith to commit ourselves to Love and to work for good that I followed on that night! To be help to others and not hurt them! I now Had The Love Of God Inside for others! There was no greater gift than that- that could possibly be for me or anyone else, and it was all free by the Love of God inside.

It is really usually a negative imagination overwhelmingly that is paranoid, fearful, suspicious and bigoted against others when this should not be the case leads to delusion. This can lead to turning inward with delusion and even hallucination in how we perceive others. (This is a theme that I will be developing and qualifying throughout the book.) Delusion of course can be very volatile and dangerous to all of us as delusion means to believe something that is not true even after we have been given better evidence to the contrary. Someone that hallucinates too where they are hearing or seeing something that is not real. In either case uncalled for misunderstandings lead to clash sometimes between people that should not exist. If we are extremely fearful and suspicious of others when the fears are not warranted then we should seek help from a doctor. There is a difference between abnormal fear where we are jumping to false conclusions about others: abnormal fear is guided by paranoid fear in itself whereas within normal fear one is more logical

aturn

and factual before jumping to false conclusions. If we are not getting along with others well enough because of abnormal paranoid suspicions of others all the time then we should seek professional help so that we can be healthy mentally again. With the right professional help we can learn not to be sometimes irrational in a negative way about others and get back into the real world. Learning a good attitude that comes from love inside and a positive attitude towards others in general is significant in helping us to "Walk On The Water" in everyday life continuously! Confidence is a booster and Love Conquers all!

Introduction:

I for one happen to be an extreme optimist about what is possible to help those with schizophrenia to overcome delusional thinking, get back in their right mind, and become healthy productive citizens! Say Hallelujah for progress in this regard that's been going on! It was just a short time ago-just 70 yrs. ago in the past that most of the people aturn that were thought be significantly schizophrenic were locked up in mental hospitals for life. And what a tragedy of course because with the right help of a counselor, education and anti-psychotic drugs most of the people that get labeled a schizophrenic can improve greatly. There is much work to be done yet to improve the condition even further for those who have suffered schizophrenia, and this includes top notch researchers like I am trying to aspire to, to find more ways to get delusion to just go away in people who were thought to be incurably psychotic for life. We will continue our efforts-those who are working to end delusion on this earth to keep trying to end the mental torment of delusion and psychosis. We want everyone on this earth eventually to just rise above delusion and psychosis and live in the dazzling sunlight of reality and enlightenment! Let's keep pushing for this to happen! Praise God for the progress that we have made so far! We won't be satisfied till everyone is well from this disorder. I want no one left behind in darkness, hell, and mental torment of mental illness!

Introduction continued:

aturn

I want the true meaning of schizophrenia to be understood by a tenth grader on up thru college because all of them will be experiencing growing pains psychologically along the way- many of them that enter at least a mild level of mental illness that attaches itself to them till they can become more worldly-wise and ditch the worst of its symptoms and be right back in reality at a yet much higher level of conscious awareness than a high schooler. We learn to work harder than we ever did before and make new friends that amounts not to just the old gang or hangouts of our youth but people from a much broader range of background, together with zeal for a better society that values "education" and a "work ethic" both; progress for man with us now becoming the "real make it happen" for our society. Progress" for us all with our well-intended actions-that literally indeed change the world for the better! Nature may shock you with the changes that you go thru up ahead in developing a more intelligent, rational creature with better more integrated actions that literally say love, comradriship and shared dreams of a better society, as we keep growing to a much higher level of conscious awareness! Changes are coming that will make you fit as a young adult that will enlighten you and make you fit for the rest of your life if you can just learn to accept

aturn

the "new" of change that includes education and constructive criticism sometimes that it takes to make a real man out of the boys and girls that we once were: till as an adult now think at a plateau of conscious awareness that works like it should in understanding reality and people and knowing how to act accordingly for all circumstances! May you be blessed in all ways throughout your life remembering to love everyone with a Big Love from above! Amen!

Table of Contents:

Preface

Introduction

Chapter 1 Just What Is Schizophrenia

Chapter 2 One Hundred Examples Of Delusion

Chapter 3 Developing A Fuller Meaning To The Behavior Of Others

Chapter 4 Becoming An Actor On A Stage

Chapter 5 Caught up in a world of symbolism

aturn

Chapter 6 Reading The Signs Of The Behavior Of Others

Chapter 7 The Games People Play

Chapter 8 The Road

Chapter 9 The Influence Of Trauma From Our Past That Affects Our Present Behavior

Chapter 10 The Need For Employment

Chapter 11 The Lack Of Literacy And Education

Chapter 12 The Need For Higher Education

Chapter 13 Several Disorders That Interrelate With Schizophrenia

Chapter 14 Past And Present Treatment For Delusion

Chapter 15 Who Were And Now Are The Most Major Researchers On Schizophrenia And Delusion

Chapter 16` My Ideas On Rising Above Delusion

Chapter 17 Education On Schizophrenia

Chapter 18 Attitude

aturn

Chapter 1 Just what Is Schizophrenia?

According to Gale Encyclopedia Of Nursing And Allied Health, "Schizophrenia is a psychotic disorder (or a group of disorders) marked by severely impaired thinking, emotions, and behaviors. Schizophrenic people are typically unable to filter sensory stimuli may have enhanced perceptions of sounds, colors and other features of their environment. Most schizophrenics, if untreated gradually withdraw from interactions with other people, and lose their ability to take care of personal needs and grooming." In effect then Schizophrenia is a mind that is confused about what is real that in turn affects how one thinks or behaves accordingly that puts their mind in decline;

The Five Symptoms Of Schizophrenia:

Well how does this sickness come about? To begin with we should first know there are five symptoms of behavior related to this aturn disorder. According to The Diagnostic Statistical Manual these five symptoms are: 1) **delusion** 2) **hallucination** 3) **disorganized behavior** 4) **disorganized speech 5) negative symptoms.** According to the DSM 5 we define "**delusions** as fixed beliefs that are not amendable to change in light of conflicting evidence. Their content may include a variety of themes (e.g., persecutory, referential, somatic religious, grandiose)." The second symptom of schizophrenia is **hallucination.** According to the DSM 5, "**hallucination** has perception-like experiences that occur without an external stimulus. They are vivid and clear, with the full force and impact of normal perceptions, and under voluntary control." The third symptom of schizophrenia is According to the DSM 5 as it pertains to **disorganized behavior** "Grossly disorganized or abnormal behavior may manifest itself in a variety of ways, ranging from childlike "silliness" to unpredictable agitation. Problems may be noted in any form of goal-directed behavior, leading to difficulties in performing activities of daily living." The fourth symptom is disorganize speech. "Disorganized **speech** (formal thought disorder) is typically inferred from the individual's speech. The individual may switch from one topic to another (derailment or loose associations). Answers to question may be

aturn

obliquely related or completely unrelated (tangentiality)." The fifth symptom of this disorder is negative symptoms. "**Negative symptoms account for a substantial portion of the morbidity associated with schizophrenia but are less prominent in other psychotic disorders. Two negative symptoms are particularly prominent in schizophrenia : diminished emotional expression and avolition diminished emotional expression includes reductions in the expression of emotions in the face, eye contact, intonation of speech (prosody), and movements of the hand, head, and face that normally give an emotional emphasis to speech."** Pg. 87-88

Of these five symptoms delusion by far should be thought of as the most prominent in terms of severity and danger to yourself or others. Delusion is the most major way to exit reality as we will all come to know it is a passionate but false belief in the face of overwhelming superior evidence to the contrary.

According to Dorothy Ruiz a popular contemporary researcher on schizophrenia says-"schizophrenia is delusion..."

.) Next to delusion in terms of its prominence and severity as a subtype of schizophrenia is hallucination. Hallucination is to see, hear, taste feel, or smell something that is not real but just imagined. It really overlaps with delusion too in at least in some cases. For example if someone is presently having a delusion about others they may also see hear, see, taste, smell, or feel-that which is not real or then experience a hallucination then at the same time. For example suppose someone thinks based on their personal ESP that George Washington has risen from the grave-that would be an example of delusion about George Washington coming back to life, and then he also thinks he sees ole George around at places they go when he apparently just imagined it. He sees George Washington everywhere he goes when it is not real! This of course then would also be an example of delusion and hallucination together.

How many different kinds Of Delusion Are There?

Next, it happens to be the case that in actuality there are really as many different kinds of delusion as there are different ways in which one's mind can be tricked into believing a falsehood when superior evidence is in front of you to the contrary.

There happens to be though some particular kinds of delusion that are more common than others. According to Melinda Smith in

aturn

Schizophrenia Symptoms, Signs, and Coping Tips there are four particular kinds of delusion that apparently stand out as the most common: They are (1) the delusion of reference. (2) the delusion of persecution (3) the delusion of control, and (4) the delusion of grandeur). Delusion of reference-"A neutral environmental event is believed to have a special and personal meaning. For example you might believe a billboard or a person on TV is sending you a message mean't specifically for you."

Delusion of persecution- "Belief that others, often a vague "they" are out to get you. These persecutory delusions often involves bizarre ideas and plots (e.g. "Martians are trying to poison me with radioactive particles delivered through my tap water")"

Delusion of control- "Belief that your thoughts or actions are being controlled by outside, alien forces. Common delusions of control include thought broadcasting ("My private thoughts are being transmitted to others") thought insertion (Someone is planting thoughts in my head") and thought withdrawl ("The CIA is robbing me of my thoughts")

aturn

Delusion of grandeur- Belief that you are a famous or important figure, such as Jesus Christ or Napolean when this is not true. Alternatively, delusions of grandeur may involve the belief that you have unusual powers, such as the ability to fly.

It is also important to remember that of the four kinds of delusion just alluded to that there are just two that stand out as by far the most common and sometimes overlap. They are the delusion of reference and the delusion persecution. The delusion of reference means that you are reading the potential private messages from others that are usually thought to be negative. The delusion of persecution means that you are afraid that others are conspiring to hurt you. This same person may turn inward making a world and false explanation of their own that obviously to almost anyone else does not hold believability. These two delusions go hand in hand with each other and occur quite frequently in people.

There is yet one more important distinction that I should make before I move on to the competing theories about what causes schizophrenia. That distinction is between that of non-bizarre delusions vs. bizarre delusions. A non-bizarre delusion according to

aturn

the Cleveland Clinic- Non bizarre delusions involve situations that could possibly occur in real life, such as being followed, deceived or loved from a distance. These delusions usually involve the misinterpretation of perceptions or experiences. In reality these situations are either untrue or are highly exaggerated. According to Webmd a bizarre delusion by contrast is something that could never happen in real life, such as being cloned by aliens or having your thoughts broadcast on TV. A person who has such thoughts might be considered delusional with bizarre type delusions.

Competing Theories On What Causes Schizophrenia:

First there are two major schools of thought reflecting on the potential cause or causes of schizophrenia. They are (1) the biological (2) the social, environmental and psychological factors together behind schizophrenia. Yet also there is a

aturn

third position on this same issue (3) that believes that schizophrenia cannot be said to exist at all since there is lack of solid biological support for its existence as a disease. Since this is the case it can't be said to exist at all as a disease anyway. (The first two and not this third position have the most support in believing nonetheless.)

1. The biological proof and support for believing in the existence of schizophrenia:

First Two theories that are biological in terms of the explanation for the occurrence of schizophrenia: First an indirect one that may not tell us the most ultimate cause of schizophrenia at all but has proven to know the likelihood of when it might occur. This would be research and subsequent data that points to the fact that if you have schizophrenia in your family tree you or other family members that followed may be likely to get it than in another family that does not

aturn

have this disorder in their family tree.   A Quote **By NHS** says:

Genetics

Schizophrenia tends to run in families, but no single gene is thought to be responsible.

It's more likely that different combinations of genes make people more vulnerable to the condition. However, having these genes does not necessarily mean you'll develop schizophrenia.

Evidence that the disorder is partly inherited comes from studies of twins. Identical twins share the same genes.

In identical twins, if a twin develops schizophrenia, the other twin has a 1 in 2 chance of developing it, too. This is true even if they're raised separately.

In non-identical twins, who have different genetic make-ups, when a td environmentawin develops schizophrenia, the other only has a 1 in 8 chance of developing that unique condition.

While this is higher than in the general population, where the chance is about 1 in 100, it suggests genes are not the only factor influencing the development of schizophrenia

From Quest Bright Treatment centers in an article called "Does schizophrenia run in families?" Family history in general is **the number one predictor for schizophrenia**, and by a environmental-wide margin. Among the general population the likelihood of any particular individual being diagnosed with schizophrenia is right around one percent, but that number rises by several percentage points when family members have also been diagnosed with the condition.

Yet another biological explanation for the existence of schizophrenia that is quite direct and unique that has some viability to it in terms of believability to the masses is the theory that smaller frontal lobes at the front of your skull may be a cause for schizophrenia. As ludicrous as this may seem at an initial thought on this issue, they apparently have proof of a correlation between those who have schizophrenia and the size of your frontal lobes being smaller accordingly. This theory however still needs much more compelling proof of it in order for it to be a widely accepted theory. Anyways here is a quick rundown on this theory including what proof there is of it. In Structural abnormalities in the frontal system in Schizophrenia: a magnetic resonances imaging study: "Thirty-eight schizophrenics and 49 normal controls underwent magnetic resonance imaging. Midline sagittal cuts indicated that the schizophrenics had significantly smaller frontal lobes, as well as smaller cerebrums and craniums. The findings are consistent with some type of early developmental abnormality that might retard brain growth and therefore skull growth. These findings are confirmed on a smaller sample of patients on whom we have coronal cuts. Decreased cerebral and cranial size are associated with prominent negative symptoms, although decreased frontal size is not. Decreased cranial and cerebral size was also associated with impairment on some cognitive tests. These findings are consistent with the hypothesis that some schizophrenics may have a type of early developmental abnormality associated with prominent negative symptoms and cognitive impairment. Further, the results suggest that schizophrenics may have a type of structural frontal system impairment. Thus, they provide anatomic evidence for the "hypofrontality hypothesiss".

This research that they have done that is biologically based, whether it concerns genetics or the size of frontal lobes is not sufficient evidence to believe that schizophrenia itself is caused by biological means. And we definitely don't find a complete solution to delusion this way, whereas if we are to examine the social, environmental, and psychological factors for why someone has become schizophrenic, one can more easily find a potential solution for getting oneself to rise above delusion, and this is what is most important- the mental health of the patient.

2. The psychological, social, and Environmental factors that trigger and perhaps actually cause schizophrenia.

When one is in high school everything is to a large degree as it pertains to all of your activity is laid out for you by the system if it means attending school and obeying the curfew. If you work a job or have much of a social life this might be by your own initiative, but you are definitely still a minor and your parents can still make the big decisions for you. But when we reach 18 which is college age for most people we may be soon beginning to make a lot more or decisions by ourselves! Learning to work out there in the free world and paying the bills by ourselves will come about for most people. Learning full competency on the job out in the adult working world where the expectations of you at this age may be a lot more than they were for you as a teenager. This represents a lot of change for you in terms of lifestyle and the new decisions that you will be making....!

The social, environmental and psychological causes for what at least triggers schizophrenia in someone are quite numerous. An example of a social factor that might trip schizophrenia would be social anxiety in you magnified enormously out in the adult working world whether it is just blue collar work or a professional job in business where you may have to public speak and interact with others related to business. One may decide to turn inward more than they should......! An example of an environmental factor that potentially triggers schizophrenia is working in a noisy environment in the factory where people yell at each other just to hear and aggressive and/or even angry behavior could erupt among a broad range of backgrounds and lifestyles of many different people represented right there. A psychological example of schizophrenic trigger is trauma that we experienced at a younger age that now when out in the adult working world shows up in our personality in the form of aversion from other people or overreaction to other people! Yet another example of a psychological explanation for what triggered delusion in you could have something to do with the fact that there is really a difficult phase that you are going thru (wherein your mind is hell bent on understanding the behavior of others just in everyday life as some kind of sign or message from them because their behavior could be said to have a potential double meaning to it, that you get carried away with in your imagination....! Just the way the boss smiles or where your co-worker lays his gear you take as a personal message to you that is negative......! Now I could give you a practically endless list of hypothetical examples where either the social,, environmental or psychological factors (or a combination of them) that they experience especially at the young age of late teens thru mid-twenties that they experience, but I think that I have given you enough right there to give you the idea of what might trigger schizophrenia related to the situation and/or state of mind that they are in when they become delusional.

They will be experiencing "growing pains" in terms of how to adapt to this much major change in their life in just a short time that is real! They have much to learn and sometimes that takes a little time and learning not to get fooled by the tricks their own mind seems to play on them at times. When the new tasks become undo-able for you, you really may turn inward with what started out as just a mild case of nerves to what now turns into disaster and full-fledged delusion and psychosis wherein you harbor false beliefs about others. In chapter three of this same book you are reading, I develop a case for it being that young people actually go thru a phase which is really stage of psychological development in itself that I call the "environmental shock" stage of psychological development where your mind is seeking more meaning to what goes on around you than what you might literally notice just at a glance in itself. Of course all or most young people at this age do not develop serious mental problems, but they do share common experiences of "growing pain' hardship to one degree or another where they may be having trouble adapting to working along with others without confusion or at least frustration that may be a sign of immaturity on your part. It is of course possible to turn inward too far and become delusional at any age, but it is the leap from high school into the adult world that includes major change for most of them that sometimes brings on delusion.

A fabulous article that comes up with at least the social changes that we may experience as a young adult out in the real world is called **Social Defeat that** hints at the potential frustration and perhaps negative reaction of feeling like you are losing in life! (The British Journal of Psychiatry, Volume 187, Issue 2, August 2005, pp. 101 - 102

DOI: https://doi.org/10.1192/bjp.187.2.101[Opens in a new window]
Copyright
Copyright © 2005 The Royal College of Psychiatrists)

"This editorial propsoses the hypothesis that a chronic and long-term experience of social defeat may lead to sensitisation of the mesolimbic dopamine system (and/or to increased baseline activity of this system) and thereby increase the risk for schizophrenia. The currently dominant belief that 'psychosocial stress' plays only a modest role in the aetiology of schizophrenia has become untenable in the light of new epidemiological findings…."

3. Schizophrenia Can't Be Said To Exist As A Real Disease At All? Thomas Szasz

According to professor Thomas szasz of psychiatry at the state University of New York, "He was best known as a social critic of the moral and scientific foundations of psychiatry, as what he saw as the social control aims of medicine in modern society, as well as scientism. …. Szasz argued throughout his career that mental illnesses are not real in the sense that cancers are real. Except for a few identifiable brain diseases, such as Alzheimer's disease, there are neither biological or chemical tests nor biopsy or necropsy findings for verifying or falsifying DSM diagnosis", i.e., there are no objective methods for detecting the presence or absence of mental illness. Szasz maintained throughout his career that he was not anti-psychiatry but was rather anti-coercive psychiatry. He was a staunch supporter of civil commitment and involuntary psychiatric treatment but believed in, and practiced, psychiatry and psychotherapy between consenting adults.

His views on special treatment followed from libertarian roots, based on the principles that each person has the right to bodily and self-ownership and the right to be free from violence from others, although

aturn

he criticized the "free world" as well as the communist states for their use of psychiatry."

In other words said more plainly Szasz did not actually believe that schizophrenia had even been proven conclusively and people should have the right to seek treatment from others like Szasz in which it is mutually voluntary who want psychiatric treatment. Although this wonderful eye-opening Philosophy must have kept a lot of people laughing it did not solve the problem of sick minds with schizophrenic symptoms. Whether you can prove schizophrenia conclusively with biological proof, schizophrenia is still definitely an identifiable behavior disorder by way of continued symptoms of its presence- delusion foremost! We can definitely tell when someone has a problem with delusion-its continuation – and the negative effects it has on others! Everyday too frequent of personality clashes with others may be occurring and we may be withdrawing from others into a world of our own! An obvious behavior disorder like delusion can be easily verified by simply following this same person's everyday pattern of behaviors. Schizophrenia and delusion are very dangerous and if we really care for the victim of it or those around this person we should wish for them to get psychological help when it is really in order!

Thomas Szasz is quite humorous, but that doesn't stop the disorder of delusion from being real and dangerous to us all! The state makes those that are sick in the head bad enough to be dangerous to themselves or others get help because they need it or we are simply not safe! Thomas Szasz makes some interesting observations about this disorder as well as the motives of the state, but when someone's behavior becomes so sick in everyday life we had better heed the warning signs for us all!

The Need For A Psychiatric Counselor

When young people especially but really to all at any age when a person that is acting peculiar begins to show several of the symptoms of this disorder continuously-especially delusion they need psychiatric help for themselves and the safety and well-being of us all! Once again the symptoms of this disorder are delusion, hallucination, disorganized speech, disorganized behavior, or negative behavior:

"The most common early warning signs include: 1. Depression, social withdrawal 2. Hostility or suspiciousness, extreme reaction to criticism 3. Deterioration of personal hygiene 4. Flat expression gaze 5. Inability to cry or express joy or inappropriate laughter or crying 6.

aturn

Oversleeping or insomnia; forgetful, or unable to concentrate 7. Odd irrational statements; strange use of words or way of speaking

While these warning signs can result from a number of problems-not just schizophrenia- they are cause for concern. When out-of-the-ordinary behavior is causing problems in your life or the life of a loved one, seek medical advice. If schizophrenia or another mental is the cause, getting treatment early will help" (Help guide.Org -Melinda Smith)

Keep Developing:

Now to all of us it is possible in fact to just give up on adapting to the cruel adult world that we enter during our late teens and early twenties in general, especially with all of the "growing pains" and psychological changes that we grow thru then. But now the right encouragement and the will to persevere instead of quit or give up in the face of adversity or defeat, we just might make ourselves a winner!

Finally I want to say before we move on to the next chapter that give a hundred examples of delusion- the main sub-type of schizophrenia, let me right here and now tell you that I do not suppose that the biological supporters in understanding the cause of schizophrenia will ever find the cause this way because I firmly believe that what causes schizophrenia is really hidden trauma the most that we may have locked inside us from days gone past. It gives us social anxiety inside to aversion or overreaction. We need to heal our mind by re-establishing positive relationships with others, albeit with caution that is appropriate that we need not have the same traumatic things happen once again! Learning at the same time the right tact with others to make sure we don't repeat the same mistakes that we did that lead to trauma that hindered you for the future. Also developing a good understanding of human nature in general. And then developing communication skills to reach everyone too can be quite helpful to you without dangerous commitment again. Learn to stay positive in how we treat others that is sincere and genuine is essential! Forget the hurt of the past enough to try again! Delusion can be overcome in time! I do not believe those who tell me otherwise!

Anyway it is the people that address the social, environmental, and psychological reasons for schizophrenia that are really getting people to overcome delusion permanently whether the ultimate cause of schizophrenia is biological or psychological that cause schizophrenia…….! One's "growing Pains and fears and anxieties of our youth can be overcome with just the right encouragement and better thinking without irrational fear involved. Understanding yourself and others better come with time! Delusion itself consists of strong subjective feelings that are false that lingers even after we have been given superior evidence to the contrary. This is then delusion which is a disorder that of course is dangerous but can be treated with the right professional help! We may need education and coaching about the nature of delusion and schizophrenia itself for the patient of schizophrenia also. And also personal coaching to this individual that is delusional to stay calm and rational even when were scared, and the need also to stay positive with a work ethic that's continued……!

Chapter 2   One Hundred Examples Of Delusion:

Next, I should mention that the young people growing up –especially those in their late teens and early twenties are usually going thru an "identity crisis" and are too easily confused about what to do or how to go about it for that matter. They are now learning to be rational

aturn more and follow procedures better though! But when they then wake up enough to see that potentially all eyes are upon them with the need to perform like they should they too often succumb to delusion! (Delusion of course to believe a falsehood about others when there has been better evidence to the contrary put in front of you.) Like man they still have a persecution complex that is coming to a head- that is now turning into a persecution delusion or delusion of reference- where they not only think people are out to hurt them, but now they are hell bent on reading the signs of others behavior in everyday life while they still think that others are against them in everyday life much more than what is real- and jumping to false conclusions about the meaning of the behavior of others! Inside they are crying out for help; inside of them they now are feeling afraid, angry and betrayed by others including the system itself, and have much mistrust in others in general. When if they just continue to follow thru with their constructive endeavors of work and education plus add love in their hearts for others they will develop an attitude of love in general towards others in everyday life where will then become an achiever; an Eagle scout so to speak that now has developed a normal level of trust in others, and is now not afraid of

aturn

reality or others but enjoying and digging others. The signs along the way now are more positive: love, friendship and goodwill towards others while becoming a winner! And we can all become winners with a good attitude for that matter!

    We can turn boys into men that come into their right mind by explaining that they are just going thru a phase and stage of psychological development that I think we should call **environmental shock and not acute or permanent schizophrenia**; and encouraging them to keep on truckin' with their constructive and creative endeavors- to be help not only to themselves, but others as well! Love is coming to us all and enlightenment too! God loves us all and we all count and we all have beautiful things to share as we are waking up our mind and maintain a good attitude towards others!

    I have composed one hundred short stories below describing delusion of many kinds that is quite common in young people in general to give them a better understanding of the pitfalls of it. I hope you enjoy them and learn something from them-namely foremost not to be in any hurry to jump to false irrational conclusions about others!

aturn

Example 1: New Employment

The first example involves a young person that has just gotten temporarily hired at a place where he can win permanent employment after a thirty day grace period where he must show that he is a useful worker. Well he was hired in on the assembly line in there for brakes, and he did quite well for the first couple of weeks till they forced him to change his job on the line to cover for someone that just quit his job there for a better one. This now this new job on the assembly line was challenging to this young man to say the least, but the boss told him to do the best that he could and that he should improve at it. What went thru this young man's head over the next few days while he was breaking in on this new job on the assembly line was that at least some of these people that worked on the assembly line were against him in in his plight for employment with this company. While you were starting out on this new job a couple of others that worked on it including a big guy that was never friendly to you were laughing like a hyena at your clumsiness at the task put in front of you. Was this laughing that they were doing not mean't to be

aturn

something that was seriously cynical to you or did they mean it with malice towards you? Yet a couple more people that worked on this same assembly line were whispering to each other when they were standing close to you while you were working on this new job. You immediately wondered whether this mean't that they were really talking about you and in a way that seriously cast doubt about your ability to do this now job and ultimately about whether this mean't that they absolutely did not support your chance to get hired in permanently.

On Friday you were standing in line at the time clock about to punch out for work when you noticed that up at the front of this line was this same big guy that worked on your line that didn't seem to like you. He was right now talking to someone standing right behind him. They both began to laugh together about something that you did not know at all what it could be about. Right then as they were laughing and talking together this very same big guy looked right at you while he continued to laugh. To you this was a sign that just maybe they could be laughing at you and a replacement for you was up their sleeve the next week. You of course are far from knowing this to be

aturn

the case, but a strong fear gripped you inside while he was looking and laughing at you that further convinced you that this must be the case. When you had this fear go thru your head you bother to ask yourself next inside is this a serious indication that you may not be employed here soon? In light of the fear that you felt that you might be losing your lob soon that you felt when this guy laughed at you just a second ago made you think in light of this and not the more reliable evidence going the other way, where management had bothered to be encouraging to you lately and did not say to you that you were not doing a good enough job, just because your new one was somewhat of a challenge to you should have indicated to you that in likelihood things could work out if you really wanted to stay. You the nonetheless go home on this particular weekend and get trashed on booze all weekend because you are afraid that you are going to lose your employment where you presently work soon. When you get to work the following Monday morning you are finally cautioned by management that your work was getting pretty good, but if you want permanent employment here you will not come to work with a hangover again! How stupid could you feel then?

aturn

Now I have composed a diagram, (which I show in detail in chapter 16), which reveals in just simple steps of the thought process how one entered delusion in this story just told to us. In the first step this person literally noticed that a big guy up ahead of him at the time clock while talking to someone looked right at you while laughing hysterically. In the second step of the thought process you begin to focus on any personal significance to this guy laughing while looking right at you. In the third step of your thought process you are now literally asking yourself could this guy actually be trying to give you a hint or innuendo, or message then that you just might be all done as an employee where you have just begun working a short time ago. In the fourth step of the thought process you decide that he must have been trying to send you a message that he didn't think you would be hanging out there much longer, which you then actually happen to believe is probably really true too,-which is not the truth but the guy was just laughing for comic relief and he was not insinuating you're soon departure.

Now first we can determine from this diagram that at least in some sense while entering delusion that fact that special meaning coming

aturn

alive to what you see does not in itself constitute irrationality. We all experience sometimes a potential symbolic meaning coming alive to what we literally seen, heard or thought. Symbolism or symbolic meaning to what one literally seen heard of thought is innate and infinite in possible variety to anyone that is awake. Secondly, you can literally pin-point with the help of this diagram how it is in the fourth step where one is deciding whether to believe the special meaning that came alive to them means someone sent a message. If one chooses to believe that the special meaning or symbolic meaning that came alive to you in the second step means that a message was sent to them by others when this is not the case and there is superior evidence to the contrary against exaggerations and falsehoods of bad common sense then this is to expose an irrational leap of faith in the false conclusion.

Anything is possible including that one was traumatized somewhere in there youth and does not have a normal level of trust in others that one should as a result!

Example 2:   Who's She with?

aturn

The second example of a hypothetical and ficticious story of a delusion- the delusion of ESP in this case, is about how someone imagined what was going on behind his back was necessarily true and real even just because he thought that it was real when there was superior or better reason to believe otherwise and it also turned out false.

In this particular story this guy thought that his wife was running off with the UPS driver. Several weeks before he had these thoughts a package was delivered by the UPS to their house. His wife ran to the door when the package arrived as it turned out the guy that was delivering the package was an old friend of hers from high school. They talked merrily for several minutes at the door before he went back to his truck and drove off. The guy could see from the window when the UPS driver walked back to his truck that he was right now putting a pen back in his pocket. You thought that this was odd because you were almost sure that it was not necessary for anyone to sign for the package that you received. You remembered too that he was tall and skinny!

aturn

As it was getting towards Christmas your wife spent large amount of time out shopping, and in your imagination you thought that she was meeting up with the UPS driver for a sex relationship. At first you did not believe your thought, but then after three or four trips out to get our friends and relative a present she quit bringing presents back to the house when she went out shopping, but told you she couldn't find any more presents of what she had left to buy. One night when she got home she hurried to restroom before talking to me like maybe she had some freshening up to do and then just stayed away from me the rest of the night. I really thought for sure she must have been spending time with the UPS driver. So the next time she went out you followed her to the store where she went in and was apparently shopping. After few minutes you got out of your car and went in and found that your wife was shopping in the men's clothing department. When you walked up to her she held up a man's pair of shorts that you told her you wanted for Christmas, and smiled and said, "now is this what you wanted for Christmas!" I said, "yes"! She said back I am buying them for you tonight to which you quickly said, "Great"! When we got back home after we stopped for a drink somewhere I put on these shorts for a short time till lights out came and we made

aturn

passionately love on this night. The only thing that you didn't like about your new pair of shorts was the fact they were almost too tight for you. The end!

Example 3: Competition Is Real!

You have been wanting to be rock star for quite some time! You know first of all that competition is real. You know that there are no over three hundred million people here in America, and of that three hundred million people you know that there are an awful lot of people that wat to sing and entertain in that way. Why everyone and his brother by now seems to be a professional singers that you are forced to compete against with your act. Your competition sings songs using every kind of music that you can think of and they also play guitars professionally, while you play no instrument at all. You no doubt like romance and adventure songs that you have written plenty of by now and sing at open mic. But now you also write rap songs that you are quite proud of, that you think should give you the go ahead to be a real star. They are not just any kind of rap song, but mostly concentrate on coaching the young people to make a man and a

aturn

success out of themselves! I mean these are premo drill sergeant rap songs that not only are somewhat entertaining but those that take your breath away. So if that is the case where is my delusion? My assessment that I have an act that can compete is no doubt true according to my fans and not just my imagination. This is still delusion on my part though if I think that this is necessarily going to make me a big rock star soon because once again competition is real and those that like different kinds of music other than my fabulous drill sergeant rap songs may buy the hard roc CD instead. I know I'll merge my music with a hard rock band and that will give me enough diversity to compete for the big time for sure! I'm practicing right now too! Wait a minute, I hear my dog howling! I'll work on the key…!" The end!

Example 4 Looking At Things From Other's Perspectives:

You know I don't remember since after the time of my early youth saying the rude and thoughtless things about people that are overweight. By now I have just gone thru a period in my life of being aturn over-weight and believe you me I am now more empathetic towards others that have weight problem and am not quick to judge them as lazy or sick because they are. My dad I believe had a gene pattern where it was easier to get overweight and not easy to take it off. I now have arthritis that limits the amount and kind of exercise that I can do, so I got over-weight too even if I dieted-believe you me it was living hell! With the help of a doctor I am now losing weight, but only slowly. Do you know when I was a poor white kid growing up that I at least thought that sometimes that blacks were people turned away or otherwise mistreated was because they were rude and disorderly and uppity! By now I have experienced rejection from others along the way occasionally myself, just because I was not rich or in someone personal click. I know now what it's like to be people turned away like in the Robert Plant song and don't think that the lack of civil right of anybody is anything funny at all. I do like the Billy Joel song that just about brings a tear in my eye that says, "It's all about soul, it's all about joy that comes out of heartache it's all about soul, it's all about soul" We all must learn in life how to overcome the hurt that we bore along the way in life…!

aturn

So now how could this example of a delusion really be about delusion? Well you see bigotry no doubt that I would not have to give you examples of for you to see how someone could even feel justified in wrong-headedness when they are very wrong about their false justification! Just any ignorance too though about why others do what they do can be considered delusion too! Honest! Put yourself in the shoes of others before you judge them falsely! God bless those who will be a friend once in a while to others in a cold cruel world!

Example 5 The Delusion Of The Liberal Party:

The people that are in the liberal party are preached at that a living wage should come along for all jobs by now. People need a good living to get by ok in life and they are not just commodity or one cost in making the product, but a real person whose chance to survive should not considered a joke. Well this all sounds real good in itself and I agree that a business should give you the best wage that they can but relative to how much money is going thru the business. A small shop does not have billions of dollars in the company that make it possible to give you enormous pay and stay in business, like the

aturn

automobile industry has going thru their hands where the wage is significantly higher. Then too the value of labor is associated with what role you play in many cases- a common laborer for example is not going to get the same pay as an engineer. Education can be vitally important for making a good living sometimes. Then too a dollar and cents analysis of the cost themselves will determine wage. A business goes into business to make money, but when a business becomes not profitable then they go back out of business. This is a reality that the liberal party is ignoring, but it of course is real. I believe that business should try to give you the best wage that they can, but this is contingent upon the costs of the business and the overall profit that business is making too! To tell me that labor can outprice themselves without consequences is not true! The sinister plan on the part of business to keep you poor with a low wage is in many cases just not true too!

Example 6: Delusion Of The Conservative Party

Well now in order for the government to pay for even it's most vital services we need taxes collected from the citizens of this country. The rich claim that they have to pay more than their share of the taxes and

aturn then the money goes for social programs that like the welfare state that they don't approve of, and they don't owe anybody a living with the government's tax money. Using the government for social programs for the poor is not the right idea and should be ended immediately. The delusion of the conservative party is as I see it that they think that all socialism is "bad entirely"- "in itself evil"-(that is a lie), obviously social security where people save money for their retirement is why the economy didn't collapse three or four times since the time of FDR and without Medicare and Medicaid old people simply would not be able to afford their medicine. Can you think of anything more horrific? Why aren't the republicans big enough to admit that we need most of the socialism that we have instituted now to adapt to the modern world for all of us! Now if you wat to complain that some social programs are detrimental and un-necessary for our well-being that is well taken. Do we really owe a check to someone who can work and will not? I don't think so! And yes someone has to pay the taxes and that includes those that saved for social security while someone keeps robbing the fund! Who is that? All socialism in itself is not evil, but the reality of the times in certain ways! Even though we all hate taxes and I supported the president's

aturn

tax break for all of us even though I was told to do otherwise! I think that business has the right to make money and may the plight of capitalism live on! God bless America! And one more thing let's not use coal in this country again as it is terrible pollutant……….!

Example 7 Total Objectivity in understanding Delusion:

It of course takes total objectivity in order to arrive at true conclusions consistently about anything, including behavior. As it pertains to delusion one could take the position that what motivated someone to not get along with others is because they simply have a bad attitude towards others that then colors their thinking negatively. It is no doubt true that as it pertains to attitude in general that a positive attitude can go a long way in helping one get along with others that, while a negative attitude towards others can potentially bring on more personal conflict with them. But by the same token delusion in itself is not necessarily a bad attitude at all, but it is in itself a sickness where our mind is tricked into believing that which is not true- attitude can be said to be just one major contributing factor for

aturn

how someone could be said to delusional. When one enters a

delusional state of mind, one is filled with subjective fears or

passion, wherein they hold onto a particular belief, even after superior

evidence to the contrary has been put in front of them, but why is, is

not always directly apparent. There are indeed many reasons for why

someone might cling to a false belief that are brought on by social,

environmental and sociological factors that make one really think in

there head something that is not the case. Just one psychological

factor for this could be caused by trauma somewhere in there past.

Suppose for example that someone that was older and bigger bet

them up all the time as a child. Then, now after all of these years you

refused to work with a big guy on a job that was mean. Now this big

aturn

guy never showed any signs of threatening anyone nor showed any physical abuse to anyone, but did do effective work. Now it would be thought to be going overboard by almost anyone that you would refuse to work with him, but in your own mind you remember being beat up repeatedly by a bully in the family and you now simply did not trust this guy. This would be seen by many if not most a ludicrous ad irrational fear that you should overcome and just work with this guy nonetheless and make your money to survive. Delusion cannot directly be linked to just this one factor of trauma, but this is definitely something that influences how people will respond to others for maybe the rest of your life, unless the memory heals!

Example 8: A Delusion Of Reference:

A delusion of reference of course is a particular kind of delusion that when you look around you in the same environment that you are in you will notice special meaning coming alive to what you see whether it is living or dead matter that we are referring to. Now w/o overcomplicating things here all this really means is that when we look around others in particular that we may witness or hear in the same environment are really trying to communicate or send us a message -

aturn

not with words, but with body language, sounds, or presence itself to deliberately symbolize meaning that conveys some kind of hint, innuendo, insinuation or pun with the behavior that they are exhibiting right in front of us. In other words others behavior for instance mirrors a picture coming back to the victim of delusion of special meaning coming alive to others behavior, plus it includes the false conclusion on their part that someone must have been deliberately been trying to send them a message when it's just not the case! You never know though right? (This phenomena has now been updated to be called the delusion of communication if one chooses to call it that instead.)

   Anyways here is the story itself that I have to present to you that includes several delusions of reference (or delusions of communication if you will) that someone entering delusion experiences during their excursion out driving the day before Halloween! You are a guy and you happen to have been hurt by a female that you are still very much in love with. I mean you think about her every day and is it is only the time that keeps increasing from the time that you broke up with her that makes you feel less hurt

aturn

than you did then on the day you broke up. Well anyways you happen to be driving down the road when you notice a female in a purple dress that has the same hair color as the female that you broke up with-brown that is also right now embracing and a kissing with a tall gentlemen. Even though you can tell for sure that it is not the same female that you love so much it still really reminds you of her and the mental pain instantly goes thru you about her when you witness this. You tell yourself that you are going to overcome the hurt inside of you about her. As you continue to drive you are thinking about how you need your car washed and vacuumed even if you were going to be dating another female anytime soon. I mean your car really needs a good cleaning inside and out. Just then as you are having this thought a van with words on the side of it Bob's carwash on Seventh Street in Dunker-town NY. You think that sure is a peculiar coincidence that there was a carwash advertisement on the side of a van just as you were having these thoughts about your car needing washing and vacuuming. Anyways as you continue to drive you think about how it is the case that if you ever ran into this same female that you love so much with another guy that you will probably break apart. Just then at an intersection that has a green light in your favor as you began to

aturn

drive thru it that you notice out of the corner of your eye coming the other way that sitting up in the front of a Chevorlet truck a female sitting up close to a guy driving this vehicle that you think is probably her boyfriend. IN all honesty you don't think that it is really the same female that hurt you in love, but it sure hurts like the dickens inside nonetheless! YOU now are suspicious that this Chevorlet truck going the other way and the female by the side of the road hugging and kissing another guy was really something that was being staged to you by the undercover police to hurt your pride. Like you think that they are bored bum in essence going out of there for a little change from someone that is your competitor in music….! What a scary thought ha?! When you get almost home you see someone out of nowhere that is another female with a different hair color out of nowhere appear just for a couple of seconds to be walking along the side of the road that then vanishes again not to be seen any more by you. You think gee this is just one day before Halloween and I am having my first hallucination in my life right here and now! Wow! Anyways when you get home you go inside and listen to the messages on your phone. You get message from this same female that hurt you so bad in love recently that said that she was wanting to make up with you and do

aturn

you want to go to a Halloween dance with her tomorrow night. You call back her house even though she is still working this time of day and leave a message back. You say, "Yes, you are my candy honey and you got me wanting you...!" The end

Example 9 A Delusion of Persecution:

A delusion of persecution is when we think that others are against us and that they are in one way or another are trying to lean on you to hurt in one way or another when it's really not the case. This sometimes overlaps or goes hand in hand with a delusion of reference.

Suppose that you had just been transferred to another department at work and after working for just couple of weeks in the new department you are just disgusted to the point that after working where you have for almost fifteen yrs., and having the time of your life working in the department that you were just in for over ten yrs. till they just cut out and shut down all of the production in that department for good. There will be no going back there, even if there are other departments left beside the one that you are now working in

aturn

that you may bid on one of them in the long run of things! Things just weren't the same in this new department. Your co-workers were not very friendly to you; even when you had a problem that you had to be helped with to get the job done right they were only as helpful as they had to be. One day you were feeling so sad in fact you told yourself that you were having a case of the blues. Just as you were having this thought you see a guy coming the other way that works in the same department that you just now noticed was wearing blue shirt that you prior to o this day had not noticed. All in all when you first started out in this department you were unable to find peace of mind or enjoy the job much. Bu then all of a sudden after you had been there for about a month you started making several friends in this same department and you by now had learned to drive the fork truck much better and were enjoying this aspect of the job more too! Altogether when you just hung in there following thru with doing the best that you could things di improve where you now found a new home away from home you liked it so good there. At Christmas time you stopped off at the church on the way home that you attended as a child and stood outside the building with your head down and said tears to God of thanks for letting you get settled in with peace of mind and happiness

aturn

in the new department at work! Praise to Jesus was my prayer, as I am grateful for a happy prospering life! I hope others to find happiness and prosperity by the way too!

Example 10 Coincidences

Ok., so you want to know how I could be said to have had bad day on November the 19th, 2018. Well if you want to know the truth I was leaving work at the end of the first shift and was in not too bad a mood because I had a pretty good at work and after all it was time to go home from work! Anyways when I got out on the highway on this afternoon in route home from work I noticed that there was a truck just in front of me in the slower moving lane, where I was driving just 55 miles an hour in no hurry to get home! Well this guy in front of me in the truck slowed down to just 50 miles an hour and I felt like passing him up, but there were too many cars, trucks and Suv's passing me by at the same time continuously for several minutes that prevented me

aturn

getting into the faster moving lane! I took a deep breath and thought oh this is just a coincidence and I will soon be home so I should not be upset in any way, but glad to be alive instead! I was happy to be alive when I exited from the freeway till I read the bumper sticker on the back of the next vehicle up ahead of me that said ban the NRA that was driving terribly slow- 10 under the speed limit. It really felt like the whole ordeal so far driving work was being ambushed with a rigged conspiracy of probably the undercover police to wreck my good day, just for the hell of it! Like they just about strike me like an ignorant bored bum that doesn't have any more sense or decency to just let people to just go round and round in peace when they are not obstructing or infringing on the rights of others! I know that we of course need the institution of security whether it is a patrolman or the undercover police too- the undercover police are in other roles too for a living by the way – the ones of them that are on the ball- and you would not know that they have anything to do with the police work at all. Anyways I did not know for sure that anybody that was in the undercover police deliberately just did anything to harass me, but the whole thing could really be just a coincidence. When I finally got on the next road home I had no one driving all ahead of me for several aturn blocks. I was telling myself that the real police got a tough job to do that has to be performed for us all, so we should respect and appreciate them and not hate them. Anyway just few blocks ahead of me on this country road were two semis out ahead of me going very, very slowly- about 20 miles an hour in a 40 mile speed zone. The roads here in Michigan were hilly and there was a double yellow line in the middle of the road that made it illegal to pass anyone for a long stretch of road- till it got less hilly! Anyways, even though I was read hot inside right now I was not only telling myself to stay calm, but I was thinking that I really should be grateful to be alive, prospering here in Michigan, USA and not get too uptight about a little bad weather, meaning the cars and truck that drove in front of me on the way home from work! I then thought about how I am in a minority position on crime- I tell myself that I am like George Bush senior who said, "we should feel sorry for the victim of crime and not the perpetrator of it." And this includes shit headed idiots that don't respect others certain un-inalienable rights, and this includes the right to compete in a capitalist society with your rock act too. You see I have several songs that I have written that deserves to be heard and this whole drive home felt like a conspiracy to wreck my good day- like

aturn

they had all rigged getting in my way no matter who they were. Like they were all shit-headed idiots that don't respect my certain un-inalienable rights man! Well I did not actually believe deep down this thought, but the feeling of being persecuted by others on this afternoon while driving home still lingered in me. Finally just before I got almost home and ambulance followed by two squad cars came racing the other way with their lights on and I was forced to pull over for a moment while they passed before I could continue up the road short space till I reached my driveway to the house I live in. All in all it really felt like other must have went out of their way in the road to wreck you ride home in peace! I however choose not to believe this but sure hope security don't ever play idiotic uncalled for games to others! A series of coincidences on the way home from work on this day almost got me to feel persecuted but I don't really believe a lie that anybody just played a game at all! Nobody in actuality played any game at all! It is up to me to learn tolerance and patience and learn not be an idiot myself, but a smart worldly- wise dude instead! God bless you and not fuck you to others is the right attitude! Be Big!

aturn

Example 11 Stereotyping!

We have all had a bad day, even those claim not to be bigot to other groups of people, where we could get mad enough in our head to be resenting those of another race, age, sex, or sexual preference when we get our feelings hurt bad enough by some thoughtless person that look or act different than we do. Suppose you are a civil rights member that believe in fairness and inclusion for blacks in the job -market like the democrat party talks about, but right now you are now concerned about crime the most so for the office of president anyways you are going to keep crossing over to vote republican. You still believe in fairness and inclusion for everybody that want to work though! But now after this new support for the right in politics everywhere you go and everything you do you seem to be getting feedback of rejection from blacks. It is a temptation when we people show negative signs of behavior from others of another color let's say that you will "overgeneralize" that the negative stereotype that you experienced right in front of you is indicative of all blacks when this is far from being true. Like they must all be like that, ha! This of course delusion! Most of them just want to go to work to feed their family

aturn

and at the end of the day be with them. I decided not to let a small sample of those apparently mad at me that are black keep me from loving them all! Guess what the world is as you are! Stay positive and friendly with a broad range of people and "don't let just one bad apple spoil the whole bunch for continued friendship with others! Remember that even when the stereotype that is negative is also real it does not then mean that all blacks, women or republicans are bad people! It just doesn't meant that! Now I'll tell you who the real villains are……!

Example 12 The Time Change

In my hometown of Quinton there was a time change moving the clock back an hour, to add an hour of light for those on their way too work or school in the winter. Anyways I live alone and I had not heard about the time change from the news or word of mouth from anyone. Well anyways to make a long story short I was to run into a few hurtful and/or embarrassing experiences on the Sunday morning following the time being set back at midnight the night before. Now on this particular Sunday morning in early November I went to the restaurant at 5:00 AM sharp to get a cup of coffee. Well of course they were not

aturn

open due to the time change. Well, the first thought that I had was that one or another of the crew members that was supposed to be at work here this morning had overslept or got sick. Then I thought as I just plain drove away from the drive thru and on my way in route back home I thought "well no big deal I"ll just make coffee at home this morning". At high noon on this day I still did not know that the time had changed. I do not drink alcohol at home as good as ever, but I felt like going to the bar/restaurant just down the street for just one beer and sandwich before the football games came on in the afternoon. Well when I get there the door are locked even though there were a couple of cars in the parking lot, apparently from employees that were trying to get things set up inside. I immediately felt a rush of hurt, rejection, and embarrassment inside as what I were not thinking was that this must be personal on this day that they are not open up yet and "yes" they just plain don't like me! That's right like I literally patronize this place in the fall once a month on Sunday starting out at this time, and just maybe one or another of my friends that patronize the place don't like me no more. I thought I am not going to just sit in my car and see if and when they finally open, but I am going to just go back home and watch the ball game there. So that is what I did! You

aturn

know I told myself all afternoon while watching the ball games alone at my house that I should have known to know better than to open up my mouth about politics the last time that I was down there that must have apparently offended a couple of the more rigid left wingers that had both been my friend. I thought from now on if I ever get any football watching friends again I will stick to paying attention to routing for the teams while watching the games and never talk politics again. Why, I'll tell them my good joke about the New England Patriots at worst or best! By three thirty in the afternoon I was feeling so glum that I thought why I'll just have the nerve to go back down to the bar/restaurant and see if I am welcome at all. If so I will stay a while and watch the second half of the game that I had just been watching. Now this time when I went down there they were of course open. I walked in and order a cold beer among friends that asked me, "where have I been?" I said, "well I was here early at noon today intending to watch the game that preceded this one, and then go home and cut my grass but they were just not open. One of your friends looked back at you and said, "Did you know that the time changed last night?!" I said, No,.. oh! Do you know that I was wondering since 5:00 AM coffee time as everything else was closed at

aturn

this time of day except for an open all- night gas station. I was even beginning to take it personally that I thought that no one wanted to serve me. But now my faith in humanity is restored! I guess I got friends in this world after all!" Well now the moral of this story is to know the facts before you jump to false conclusions about others! Don't get shook and make false assumptions in the fast-lane that are really like delusions..! It really is amazing when you stop and think about how similar an assumption and a delusion really are. In the case both of these we may have been fearful and jump to false conclusions, but in the case of a delusion of course as opposed to an assumption we have been given better evidence to the contrary first, whereas with an assumption we may have just jumped to a false conclusion without first examining the facts. I almost lost my faith in the friendship of others for over half of it! But now everything is happy and bright again! My faith in humanity was restored! I was having most of the elements of a delusion of rejection or persecution till I was presented with the fact that the time changed, which or course explained the whole thing for me! I am really loved by others must apparently be the case.

aturn

Chapter 13 A Brotherhood of Man!

Some say a brotherhood of man is just a fantasy that should not and does not really exist- that it's every man or woman for their own self and there is no real force that unites us in love for each other! Now not that we can always trust anybody ultimately, but something as positive as the brotherhood of man does exist for me. I once met a tall guy that I almost despised-that I thought wanted me to be afraid of him till I caught the subtleties of his sense of humor and so ne instead we are the best of friends. I had heard growing up that many blacks just wanted to be in crime and were unruly people! But as I kept growing up I realized that they they could be your best friend sometime when you really need one. "you just call on me brother when you need a hand, we all need somebody to lean on!" they have been a friend of labor and the poor and they have toughened the psych in America in sports especially. Who's your bro sometimes on a bad day? Remember that! And I hear words that the Chinese don't love us and that the plight human rights for Hong Kong and all of China too is futile. But when I go to my favorite chines restaurant I say a

aturn

prayer for their happiness and prosperity and just know deep down inside that those that live in China or Japan are beautiful people and that the world is as you are! Think love for man everybody! Right now it is not easy to feel forgiveness towards the people that live in the Arab world sometimes after the war of gulf desert storm and Iraq. But do you know what I was on the phone conducting business the other day and I there was a guy with a dialect that I'm sure made me think that he was from the middle-east. Well he solved all my business problems on that day even though he did not have to. He was kind and considerate with foresight in business with a heart just like a sweet heart! And haven't the Saudi's been our friend and even Egypt most of the time and Israel or close ally! And aren't there plenty of good people throughout the middle- east that have love and compassion in them- virtues and high ideals for man. " Take a look on the good side my friend, and straighten out in your mind..!" The middle- east has economic problems and we should love them and not hate them. Economic depravation brings despair, but goodwill of many kinds brings hope and possibility! We should keep loving each other all over the world and not judge each other by the negative actions of a few or minority of people, but keep on reaching out to

aturn

others all over the world with your heart, knowing that there are many, many, many good people in every country and not be filled with delusion that it is just about competition on or a dog eat dog world, but respecting the human rights of our friends all over the world even as God hath taught us love everyone. Route for other happiness all over the word and do not believe the lies of Satan that hate greed, selfishness and blind passion can stop the good from loving each other all over the world and yes creating brotherhood and eventually utopia here on earth!   May you see the real light that love-brotherly love can and will overcome the hate and ill-will fueled by negative gossip or just plain indifference. "Only love is a reason, everything else is illusion!" My good Italian friend who has now gone on used to punch me in the arm after telling him my plans to be a winner at twenty one and smile and say, "opportunity knocks" Well I now wish for opportunity for all that lifts them poverty and despair! And may we never stop loving each other with brotherly love!

Example 14 Taking It The Wrong Way!

aturn

O.k. so you are a karaoke singer and song writer that is truly aspiring with your musical ability. You are becoming one of the very best karaoke singers in the town, and you are also coming into your own as a songwriter to the point that you now the courage to sing in open jam once a week. Well anyways at the karaoke bar that you sing in most of the time the karaoke disc jockey suggests that you bring in a CD that minus's you vocals on the latest CD that you wrote and sang, and sing them instead of karaoke songs that you have been singing at karaoke. It makes you feel like a cheat for sure that you will be able to sing some of your own songs at karaoke when nobody else will as far as you know. Well anyways after subtracting the vocals off of your latest CD of originals that you of course bothered to do, you sing one of them at karaoke just like it were a karaoke song. It went over good and a lot of people applauded like they usually do when you sing karaoke. You rationalize in your head that that this is ethical even if you don't know whether other aspiring karaoke singers are going to be give the same opportunity, because after all you have been set back when you should have been put ahead as a singer and songwriter to the point you were really commercial by now! Anyways after you sang like this for just one time the new karaoke disc jockey informed you aturn that this was an unfair practice against other karaoke singers since they cannot do the same thing. He said the bar has no interest in changing it official policy that it is strictly karaoke that one sings at karaoke and they will make no exceptions to this rule from now on. Well you felt hurt like you could not imagine because you got your expectation up for a miracle over this till it was shut down. You originally took it as just a hint to keep pushing with your music, but now it was futile! And what good could come out of this! You are now resenting this bar/restaurant where you knew so many karaoke singers and other friends in general. You are now just about thinking of quitting singing there altogether! But then I sang with this track in the background at open jam and the crowd went wild. After this I now think that the former karaoke disc jockey was just trying to indeed just to push me along with my music in general. I Now I don't resent him! I still sing karaoke at this same place, but I will be wary of them all just the same!

Example 15 Cursed!

aturn

You were a steel worker in Pittsburg Pennsylvania that definitely had a bad day! It started out on this day that before work you looked at your mail from yesterday for the first time and you noticed that you were sent a double size utility bill when you know you owe only one month's bill. It is too early when you leave for work to first call the utility company on the phone to try to get this corrected. This issue will have to wait till you get back home from work when hopefully you will get it confirmed by them that indeed you only owe one month's utility bill to them. You already had a dark cloud hanging over your head so to speak on this morning because you realized in your head when you woke up this morning that it is probably too late to find a new romance from a female that you really love and appreciate-one that you care about in a serious relationship. You have the negative thought on this day that it is just not going to happen; that all of the good women in this world are taken already! Maybe you can find a pig or flousy that you can shack up with that will steal all of your money instead of love and appreciate you like that someone that really does care about you! The Good book says in Proverbs 31 "A good woman who can find?" This makes you feel a sad strand in your head that is cast in your mind that is to last all day long. You know the

aturn

company is leaving too soon and you will be on the unemployment line waiting for enough money to pay the bills hopefully...! You really feel on this day that you must be a damned person! At work on this day things did not improve much as you were shorthanded on workers in your department just a little bit and had to hustle like a nut all day. By the end of the shift though you were feeling OK till you remembered while standing at the time clock that all you had to look forward to on this night was wrestling with the utilities company on the phone about how much you owe them. Just as you were about to punch out the union steward walked right up to you and said Dwight I got great news for you the company is now not moving next year but expanding and for a long time we should all be employed. Well to make a long story short you were elated with joy over this- you now had much to look forward to- all of the things that money can buy! Prosperity is back on for you! "Yahoo you think!" You are proud of yourself for following thru with the endeavor of survival like you should! You are one proud American on this day! You are not cursed, but a continued winner! You remember a quip from Evangelist Oral Roberts from TV on Sunday morning when he used to say "something

aturn

good is going to happen to you!" There are tears of joy as you leave work on this day! The end!

Example 16   I've Been There, That's why I'm Here?!

When I stop and think about the wasted time that I've spent drinking I think that in one big sense it is a reproachful thing. In all honesty I think that a little alcohol is ok and good for you. It keep people mildly cheered up and enthused with life. The problem is that addiction is real and it happens the hardest of workers and the best of people if you use. The consequences of course can wreck and devastate a life! This constitutes the paradox and ambivalence of this double edged sword! Ok I was a landscaper up in Montana in my twenties when I became addicted to beer for three or four years before they put me in a program and got me off the stuff for a long break and then moderation only after that! The reason that I bought my first case of beer at twenty five isn't because I drank six to ten shots a night or something ridiculous. But I found when I would go out to the bar that when I was talking to a friend I sometimes wanted three of four beer instead of just one or two. Also I was working on the music for my first real hard rock recording that I wanted to

aturn

practice for in the evening at home, and I reckoned that few beers would keep me there instead of out in the road. So now my motives for wanting to drink at home drove me to my first case of beer and not my obvious growing addiction all by itself! Anyways it was not long before I was drinking every day four to ten of them as I stayed home all night and practiced my guitar playing and singing. After more than two years of this pattern of behavior my alcohol began to affect my ability to keep up and I consistently practically had a hangover that by now made me look sick first thing in the morning there even though I was the best employee that you could find still anywhere. This is when if not sooner I should have gotten help from a doctor and/or the state with my permission and not plunder on with booze in excess sometimes for one more year till finally cut my first musical recording of my singing and playing my originals. It was called Hard Rock Is The Best! The entire last year before I actually cut this CD I was now moody and thought that people were against me. I was hating the state because I was in denial and my situation with alcohol had progressed to the point I had to have real help soon or I would be in trouble. I had distorted thoughts about people where I just did not appreciate, love, and want to tolerate them. I thought people were

aturn

against me, when this was just not true. A short time after I cut this CD I was arrested at work when I got there for a hangover that was atrocious. I did not know that I was even over the limit when they administered the test It was .15 which is way over the limit even though I had not drank since the night before..! They put me in a program for alcohol and I was not allowed to drink for two years. After that I went back to a celebration drink sometimes but never again hallow leg drinking, let alone on a regular basis! For me moderation is the key for the rest of my life. I am not happy if I cannot have beer once in a while but all the time and in large quantities even if at home, "NO"! So why now am I telling you this and what does this story have to do with delusion?! First of all I I want to testify to the next generation you don't have to buy a case of beer or other large quantities of it just because you like a beer. I was delusional in that I thought that others now were against me when it was not true because I was carrying too much alcohol in my head. Alcohol in excess makes for a delusion –filled person and that is a fact. The Good Book says, a false balance is an abomination unto God, but a just weight is His delight! We need to be centered and balanced and sober! Let's

aturn

get smart in our life and keep redeeming the times for all of us! Let's stay help to others and not be grief…..Amen!

Example 17 Delusion From Spectating Sports

    Coloring the truth with falsehood that was perpetrated by our own irrational analysis as the initial cause of it is of course precisely is what delusion is: Ok. now I am from Elkhart, IN where I still reside and work there too in the RV industry. I assemble RV's about fifty hours a week for fairly good pay. Well anyways come Sunday I like to watch the football game at the pro level.

I have never been a big Kansas Chief's fan, but a die hard Oakland Raider fan instead. John Madden was there coach. The quarterback was of course Kenny Stabler- the snake. The ends were Cliff Branch- the speedster, Dave Casper- the big guy who also played for Notre Dame, and Fred Belitnikoff – the hands like glue hippie. Also there was Pete Banasak- the fullback, and on defense as corner back was Jack Tatum. These people of course were the fine men that made things work right for Oakland. But then too there was the very brilliant coach for Kansas City Hank stram and a fine quarterback in

aturn

Lenny Dawson. Well now at elven yrs. old I had a simple-mindedness mentality while watching the game I liked the Oakland Raiders so very much, and disliked their rivalry Kansas that I literally hated the chiefs to the point there was serious animosity inside of me for their coach and players! "Ew the chiefs, they are the enemy!" This hatred for the chiefs coach and players turned out to be real contempt for them on my part. Where I was not realizing that they are really a good bunch on both teams and this game was all in good fun anyway! I just had to take it so personally because the chiefs sometimes had their day winning out there too. This blindness and hatred that I had for Kansas City you might as well call delusion. It lasted into my late teens when I was no in college and I by then used to think, "Did I really hate these fine people from the Chiefs team and coach over a ball game?" I was now ashamed of my eleven yr. old antics where I actually threw a fit Oakland didn't win and I would seriously despise the whole Chief's organization including coach and team players! God forgive us of simple minded hatred towards other! May God truly bless the Kansas City Chiefs and the fine people of Kansas is my sincere prayer!

aturn

Example 18 Delusion From Spending Too Much Time Alone

When I hear of these horrific crimes that people commit including mass murder to innocent people I think to myself "woe now that crazy. Oh my God how could someone ever get in such a state of mind as to just kill innocent people?" Well I don't know for sure or anything like it but I know that delusion can very easily take over in the mind of those that spend too much time alone-especially those that are considered unstable to begin with. I consider myself a normal person and I do not have a criminal record beyond traffic violations in all honesty. Even though I am not perfect and I do not think that laws are always exactly how they should be written or enforced either one. I really think myself to be a good person that respects the integrity of law as best I can and I know I want a good world too! It's not always the law though if I get a bitch in my head about whatever, but people in general from any walk of life or any neighborhood background that can make me mad. But oh, you know now negative stereo-types of blacks or women or crooks that are rich or slothful or crooked that are poor. Anyways of course there are good people from every walk of

aturn

life, economic statis and skin color and both sexes. In fact I would venture to say that most people are basically good and not evil and we should all be considered to have certain un-inalienable rights. But now what gets in the head of someone that spends too much time alone is to perhaps dwell on the negative stereo-type of others that are turn-offs or criminal. They then say to themselves, "well now if the negative behavior that I have witnessed in a small sample of others makes it indicative of all of those with the same skin color, sex, or particular economic statis others is altogether true of an entire race of people or the opposite or even same sex, or economic statis, then of course we have deceived ourselves into a false belief that is delusional. The best remedy for this kind of thinking where you exaggerate the meaning of the behavior of based on the actions of just a few is to find somewhere to socialize more with them and get a new picture of how people can be that is a little bit more positive. People that spend too much time alone instead of socialize with others on a regular basis, can sometimes really jump to false conclusions about different about a whole race of people, or sex, or different economic statis. This of course can be very dangerous when they are unstable enough not only to exaggerate the meaning of a few, but also will

aturn

resort to violence for what they fantasize about! This is the potential tragedy of people spending too much time alone- they then dwell on these negative stereo-types of others where they see a picture that exaggerates about others that is not true.

Example 19 The Undercover And Vigilante Blitz!

Ok when I was driving down the street one car was driving in my way on each individual street that I turned that was slower than molasses. And now when I went home I noticed that there were two people were waking the other way just a short distance before I reached where I was about to park in front of the house for the night. Then as I got out of my car this female was right now walking the other way with her dog with her. When I stopped to talk to her she got up close to me and tried to smell my breath and I had not had a where my car was on the same side of the street that she was walking. God these people were being an idiot to me that was uncalled for! Sometimes I have a drink but I don't drive drunk in the road! Never! But then even if I did not have drink the night before they play the same games in the traffic all the time-ridiculous idiot shit that I

aturn

presume is orchestrated by the government just to give me a hard time because it must humor them. I don' like being driven mad any more than anybody else. And does a continuous action camera lie in terms of what it show you? What if I have actual footage of the games that people play in the road that almost certainly put them up to this to do? A couple of points going the other way is fist of course that weird bazaar things really do happen sometimes where no one went out of their way to be annoying to you at all, but it was indeed just coincidence in all honesty. The second point going in this direction is that almost certainly the undercover police have the right to protect the innocent with what they might refer to as "legal maneuvers" in the road to help safety. But now if you were really leaned on personally when it was uncalled for I am on your side! I know that to license and drive a motor vehicle in the road is a priviledge and not right according to the state, and I have learned patience and tolerance to others in the road! Just drink a lot of water on a bad day and don't bother with road raging. I wish you peace, joy, and happiness and not uncalled for harassment from the state. Amen!

aturn

Example 20 "Bad Faith":

Do you know that very much that the concept of "bad faith" in Freedom and Self Creation by Jean Paul Sartre does proclaim that people are sometimes lost in "emotion" or "will" with what they decide to do with their life in general that lacks a common sense rational analysis of the consequences of their naïve or otherwise simple behavior- where they put trust in what they should not trust and for that there are negative consequences for it. What the concept of bad faith, (or lack of good faith) usually means of course is that someone is not keeping their end of the bargain when they have made one with them. Anyways let me give you a quick story about how someone acted with "bad faith" according to the Jean-Paul Sartre definition and understanding of this concept. Let's suppose that there was young female that was a pretty student in college when she applied herself most of the time, but was right now infatuated with a young man that claimed he was in love with her very much. Well to make a long story short what he did for a living was strip dance and womanize a lot, and she thought that she could make him change if they put a ring on. Well now she was kidding herself that this was aturn the case because a short time after they put a ring on, he was cheating on her with two different women! Well now when she divorced him she had to accept that she was losing her nice she was buying over the expense and she also had to bear the reputation of being perceived by others as a little bit stupid. Anyways this what the concept of "bad faith" is about that Sartre wanted us to know about! Do you know that by the general definition of delusion that delusion means that we believe something that is not true that better rational evidence support that we do otherwise! In this story the female that got ripped off because of a relationship with someone that she probably should not have trusted because she let her emotions rule instead of her ability to think rationally and with common sense. She colored reality with a lie because it felt good to do this.....! Let's be careful, all of us not to be delusional in this way, but don't let our emotions rule our ability to reason good about an issue. The end!

Example 21 Bazaar delusions:

Steve had always been a true blue committed guy to education in particular. He was a good student that loved to read science fiction at aturn a young age. By high school though his grades had dropped off to much lower marks and he was truant from classes quite frequently. His life had moved from books to drugs including crack cocaine and yes even heroine. He now spent a lot of time alone in his room not reading books, but taking very dangerous illegal drugs that can even take your life. He had withdrawn from everyone except those he got drugs from. He was now hallucinating sometimes and had become delusional about the meaning of others. He thought others were much to guided or controlled by the church or the state, and that both of these institutions really represented repression in a very big way! He wanted to be free to do his drugs or whatever else he really wanted to without any ties to school or education let alone commitment that he should have for education at this age if you want to succeed in life. He started telling people that he knew there was life on Mars and these little green guys would soon be coming after us here on earth. When he first started telling people this incredible story of Martins coming his drug friends thought that he was kidding! But when he finally started barricading his bedroom to keep the aliens away people now thought that he believed his bazaar Martian tale. It took drug rehabilitation and recommitment towards others in a

aturn

sensible way to overcome his bad habits. His grades at school went back up and he did go to college even staying clean from bad drugs and influences on him. He was not hallucinating and full of delusion again! Just like this story reveals 'bazaar delusion" like the little green guys from Mars is coming is just not to be believed because this just as good as certainly could not happen with what we know about Mars.

Chapter 22 Non- Bazaar Delusions:

Bob was a great guy-always good to everyone- not only his friends but to everyone really! Anyways he started having the experience of feeling like he was being stalked when he would go out driving his car! It seems he thought that the undercover police were mixed in the traffic according to Bob wherever he would be out driving at that same time, and they would try to give him a hard time just for the heck of it according to Bob. Everything from driving in his way to following him down the road to whatever destination he was going to

aturn

before they would then just drive on. He told me that he had like a photographic memory of what went on in the streets when he was out driving and he could draw a picture of what they did to be deliberately annoying that to him was so uncalled for. He did like to drive quick just a little bit but other than that he always good manners in the road toward the other traffic.

    He finally would come home yelling and cussing in front of his wife and kids about what he experienced. The police finally came and put him in the hospital one time after upsetting the entire family about what he experienced and put him in the hospital for two days for a mental evaluation before they just plain released him with no attachments of court orders or dates to appear in court. He told me that he has learned much more patience and tolerance in the road and learned not to be in a hurry to jump to false conclusions about who or why the traffic behaved the way they do. He said by now I believe that what I witnessed must have just been the general traffic coincidentally converging into the road at the same place and time he did. And also if people sometimes really play games in the road that are uncalled for to him or others out driving that they will pay in due

aturn

time, whereas in the small when he is out driving now that he just ignores the implications of their behavior...! This would then be a testimony of how Bob overcame his temper in the road and learned patience tolerance, and better understanding. Non bizarre delusion can be real though when we misconstrue the meaning of others behavior and dangerous too! Thank God Bob has learned more maturity......!

Example 23 Delusion Or Assumption:

It is always of course important that one knows the fact about whatever before deciding what to believe ultimately about the truth or validity of what you may have been told. Here-say and gossip about others or whatever issue that is a lie or chip shots the full truth about whatever we do not want instead! And the concept of symbolic interactionism that focuses on the impact on what we believe related to our actual everyday process of interaction between you and others

aturn

that goes on face to face and in person may really be an eye opener, and an important factor for influencing what people believe about others, it of course does not measure up to true and accurate information like all of the facts themselves tell us about whatever issue in question. O.K. now you happen to be the supervisor of a maintenance department, even though you sing and have aspirations to be a real well-paid stage act soon with your music but at least you are a mild success anyways! The bills are paid for now that have to be you have a nice house and car and plenty of good friends already. Anyways the trash was not picked up today by the local trash haulers at where you work. When this happens it is your job to call it in that your company not get the trash picked up by the local trash haulers. Anyway when you attempt to call them up on the phone about it all you get is a busy signal. Now on this day there were two of them up in the cab even though it really was just a one person job to empty out bins like he were doing. You remember that on this same outing that you were outside kidding with them and singing one of your new comedy songs to them. They laughed hysterically at your new comedy song acapella style by you. Anyways what goes thru your head is that for a practical joke going in my direction they decided that they would

aturn

not empty the trash today or maybe in the future too even though that is a somewhat ludicrous thought. You tell your whole crew in the maintenance department that these same guys that picked up the trash the other day should probably be fired for not picking it up today! The suspicion and anger grew in you over the afternoon as you needed the trash bin emptied to put new trash in it that was spread out across the floor of the plant in overflowing bins right now! Well anyways just before you were about to leave work at the end of the end of your shift you finally get thru to their trash company and are told that the truck broke down and they are using another one right now and should be there soon. You thank them for the information and leave work in a relieved state of mind that your trash bin outside that only get picked up twice a week will be emptied still sometime today. As you pull out of the parking lot you see them coming the other way with a tired sad look on his face. You wave at him, but he does not wave back! Now here you had just believed in what your imagination was telling you all day till you knew the facts. You had raced to a false conclusion where you obviously just assumed, or then made it a bad assumption about what you thought to be the case. What made it an assumption as opposed to a delusion what you

aturn thought all afternoon is that you were not give superior evidence to the contrary, but just assumed without knowing the facts, but when presented with them then believed otherwise. It is important to realize though that one could still be labeled a schizophrenic though with just too many bad assumptions where you cross wires with others in ways where you should not all the time as a result! The end!

Example 24 Delusion And Attribution

According Oxford dictionary delusion is an idiosyncratic belief or impression that is firmly maintained despite being contradicted by what is generally accepted as a result of rational argument, typically a symptom of mental disorder. According to Oxford dictionary attribution is the action ascribing a work or remark to a particular, author, artist, or person.

Now, quite obviously these two concepts do not mean the same thing. Again a delusion is to believe something that is not true even when superior evidence tells you otherwise, and again attribution is to say who we think is responsible for an action positive or negative. But let me now give you a hypothetical fictitious example showing how

aturn

these concepts could interrelate with each other sometimes. Let's suppose that you are from the poor side of town and that you think that the rich side of town is greedy for money and personal gain, while at the same time you are sure in your own mind that they are not fair to the working and the poor in their analysis of what their earnings should be and that they won't use the government's money enough to help the elderly, handicapped, and poor like they should. You are sure in your own mind that they are not the "good people" that they try to portray themselves as being. In his own mind he attributes the economic woes of the earth to the selfish and greedy rich side of town. After he works a job as a small business owner though for a few years, and is somewhat successful, but has to put up with paying what he now thinks is more than his share of the taxes and also has had to put up with employees that were dead weight or stole from him right out of the till. He now thinks differently he did up to a point wins promotion along the way, and has to pay high taxes he by now is sure that he was naïve and wrong to almost delusional proportions about the rich that time life and more experience in the real world has changed him on. The end!

aturn

Example 25 Delusion or Confubagation?

According to Healthline," confabulation is a symptom of various disorders in which made-up stories fill in any gaps of memory." Now this does not entail someone moreover that is a deliberate liar about a situation, but someone that thru traumatic experience in the past including war does not remember exactly what happened and the mind has unconsciously fabricated a picture- (thru stories in their own head) about what went on, even though it does not depict exactly what went on. Now let me give you a fictitious hypothetical example of where someone that was a war veteran from Vietnam that had confabulation about memoires related to the war itself. This guy remembered things with his fill-in the pieces memory that did not happen. Half of his battune perished in a couple of major explosions that left him deaf and with one leg gone. When it came time to recall for a government hearing on what happened on that day he remembered some of the things that happened just prior to the bombing itself that were different than the others testifying. He did not have the current or reputation of telling lies or being delusional.

aturn

He had not deserted his post or let down his comrades in any way. The doctor and a legal authority in the service right then and there also defended him that he should not be now considered not to be a liar or delusional, but someone that had confabulation. He was and is a true war hero to this day, and as ugly as Vietnam were there were positive lessons to be learned by our whole nation from this experience. God Bless our American servicemen here and around the world protecting our freedom and helping to defend against evil empires that do not believe in human rights and freedom and justice for all. Happy Thanksgiving to all of our armed forces!

Example 26 Delusion Or Deafness?

It is of course sad that many people in our country and all over the world suffer deafness. To be deaf to one degree or another makes it more difficult to work or just enjoy yourself with others as a result. OK there was this guy that was deaf about halfway in his right ear and at least sometimes it was difficult to hear what someone said if they were standing on his right side. When he was at work sometimes if a co-worker or the foreman were talking to him in his right ear he had

aturn

trouble hearing the words right. To keep pace with others he sometimes just guessed what they said in his right ear and responded back or said nothing back at all either one when it was more appropriate to do otherwise. He was filled with terror sometimes that he was be perceived as simple, even though this was really not the case at all. Anyways he eventually got labeled a schizophrenic related to his nerves and inability to work together with others, even though he could really comprehend as good as anyone else when he could just hear what they said right. He would just glare at others when he could not hear them right! Well he got a hearing aid for his right ear that worked pretty good! All of his miscommunication with others and extreme fear and paranoia vanished from then on. The doctor that he was seeing for his mental health admitted that he was doing much better. It is safe to say that he probably was never schizophrenic but just misdiagnosed as such because of this! I wonder all the time how many people have been misdiagnosed as a schizophrenic when they are in fact it is just harder for them to hear then others? It's time to take statistics on this and do something about it to help thee deaf be able to ell and/or work along with others more too! May they all join us in our ability to hear or hear better

aturn

than they have been able to!   God Bless and prosper the handicapped, God loves them too! There is documented proof that sometimes people get mislabeled a schizophrenic by professionals when they are really misdiagnosing this person in the light of the full real truth. According to Russel L. Margolis- reputable psychiatrist, "Schizophrenia may have become a trigger happy diagnosis. A retroactive analysis of patients referred to a psychiatric clinic with an initial schizophrenic diagnosis found that about half of such diagnosis were inaccurate!"

Example 27 Delusion And The Delusional Cloud:

Jasper's metaphor of the delusional cloud pertains to a confused state of mind that someone being pulled into delusion is experiencing. Someone that is entering a delusional state of mind develops a subjective will to believe something that is just not true even when they are given better evidence to the contrary. We are to believe that this is not just a cheap trick to win on a minority position on an issue about whatever, or a way to get out of work let's say, but they really just don't understand themselves the objective factual truth to be what it really is. They are now not in reality like they should be! They

aturn

are being hooked into believing something that is demonstrate-ably false. Their ill-founded fears and suspicions or even there implausible hopes and expectations are taking over their will to understand the actual truth of a matter properly. This is terribly important to realize that when delusion takes hold of you, it really is, it cannot be treated as some kind of phony act where someone is pretending to believe something when they do not, because they really are believing that which is not true- where common sense would tell you to do otherwise! And when we attempt to explain to them that their fears, and suspicions are not true even they cannot be on the spur of the moment usually be talked out of believing what they do. They have a real illness though and it should be treated that way! Delusion of course can be very dangerous to yourself or other people as a result so we want people to rise above delusion with the help of a doctor, so that we may eventually have a "delusion free society." Amen? Amen! Ok so this guy thought that people were against him in every way. He was beaten as a child by his father till they took the child away from him. But now this kid did not give up because of this but with all diligence he got to work to put his life back together again. He was bewildered and upset sometimes, And he kept trying with a good

aturn

attitude towards others even though he was mistreated by his father, and so then this kid became successful and made plenty of good friends in the long run! He now no longer has the delusion that others are against him like he once did! Hallelujah! His cloud of confusion is gone forever!

Example 28 Delusions And Violence With Guns

Right off the top of my head I am going to say that all the beefed-up gun violence we have on TV and at the movies just might be the most major factor for gun violence in America and around the world including most if not all of the mass shootings that we have had here in America. I abhor and hate violence, but love other people! What ever happened to TV shows whether comedy or cop drama where there was real love for others on the set, and not just far-wild hate, greed, passion, and self-interest only. An interesting ficticious story about how someone thought others were out to hurt him and was planning to shoot the people at the high school that he attended years ago, but was talked out of it by Howard Stern radio celebrity in a phone call he made to him while he worked at a NY radio station on a

aturn

line that the general public could not hear. The guy confessed to Stern that he wanted to go back to his old high school where he graduated years earlier and shoot the snotty students of the kind that he went to school with. He told of memories where people that were more affluent than he was trying to rub in everyday at school. Oh and they were going somewhere economically when they graduated while he knew with the grades the and work opportunity that would really be available to him was nothing but unskilled factory work for the rest of his life. Since he has graduated he has not even been able to find factory work anywhere where it is really stable employment with job security of any kind and the pay and benefits was the bottom of the barrel. Most of the others that he graduated with are doing much, much better than he did and he felt that they were really no smarter than he were when you give him a little time and a chance to catch on, and he considered himself just as good and worthy as they are. Now Howard Stern said to him, "now you hold on there just a minute my friend and let me talk. He said now one thing for sure we don't want to blame or hurt others over jealousy and we've all been there where we thought we thought we got a raw deal compared to someone else. This notion that you have of hurting those at the high school you used

aturn

to attend will not solve your problem- killing others will only get you a life of misery in jail, if you are spared. You will regret what you did! And do you know that if you just change and take a little more positive attitude than you have right now towards others, and then think of your own long-run future you are going to be much happier your life is just beginning instead of at the end. Life is just beginning for you and yes it has its ups and downs, but if you just hang in there with a good attitude towards others in a the long run just a short time up the road from now if you want prosperity you will have it. And hey in the meantime you need to see a counselor- and that is nothing to be ashamed of- he or she will be your coach to motivate you the right way right now!" This guy of course was elated by what Stern said and today he still sees a counselor for his bad nerves, but is a new person with love in his heart for others, while becoming an old pro and a well liked person at work that has reputation for a real money dog- someone that grabs all the money in the till so to speak with his fine effort at work! He is happy and well-adjusted in his attitude towards others with love in his heart for them now and an apparent inferiority complex, self-doubts and confusion have vanished! This story should make you dance with joy as we can all keep growing up past the hard

aturn

places in our life where the sun comes back out again! Scoooba, doobie good! The end!

Example 29 Another Delusion About Violence:

I have dedicated virtually the rest of my life to helping end delusional thinking in man. You're going to say well why would someone bother to spend the rest of their life doing that? Do you know that delusion is very dangerous and keeps people from being happy also! Anyways let me tell you a story about how someone thought someone was thinking something that was not true even though better evidence told him to do otherwise. He was a sick with a bad fantasy about others! I used to see him one the way to school in morning standing across the street from the old Coca Cola building scrutinizing it like he was an engineer or maybe the heat. I, just because I am a friendly guy, would look over, wave at him, and say hi to which he would sometimes smile back at me when I did. One day, on intuition I walked right up to him and said now what is the fascination with looking over the Coca-Cola building from across the street here. He said back to me, do you know that what really goes

aturn

on from in there is drug trafficking and just between me and soon I am coming back here with a sub-machine gun and shoot all of them. I said, now you must be pulling my leg? He gave me a mean look back and said I know what I am talking about and then turned his head the other way so I would not continue with anymore conversation. I simply turned around then and walked towards school where I was headed at the school house headed straight for the guard's office to tell him what this guy told me. I was sad because he responded positively back by smiling when I would say hi to him in the past and to find out that he was sick like this was disheartening. I was presently enrolled in a logic class at school, but I could not think of any word for faulty logic that applied to what this guy was sick with but I remembered looking up a new word in the dictionary yesterday that stuck in my head right now- the word "delusion"! This word I thought I am sure applied to this guy right here and now that I was just talking to. I thought that I want to learn more about what delusion is because I like people enough not to want to see them sick but better! Amen!

aturn

Example 30 Humor about Delusion

There was this guy whose ears would pop all the time and he could not believe that it was the altitude that he lived on that could cause this to be the case because he lived in Illinois! He reckoned that someone is security had some kind of radar gun or special electronic equipment capable of making his ears pop that he did not like Anyways one day at work he got so mad first thing in the morning at work that he walked up to another employee and asked him if he knew who might have sophisticated equipment that is capable of popping your ears. The guy said back to him why that is really the minorities that are dong that to let you know that they are coming on for fairness and inclusion for them. He said back oh I should have guessed this was who was doing this. Thank you! Later on that same morning his ears were still popping so that asked another co-worker who might have sophisticated electronic equipment that is capable of popping your ears. This guy said back, oh that is the women who are doing this to let you know that the want treated like an equal and full respect. The other guy said back oh I should have known who it was who would such a thing. The afternoon came and this same guy

aturn

whose ears have been popping asks yet another co-worker who it is that might pop his ears with sophisticated electronic equipment. This co-worker said back to him that it is obvious the police are popping your ears to let you know that there is a world at large and consequences for potentially deviant behavior. To which he said back oh I should have known it was the heat trying to make sure I'm good. Then finally at the end of the shift when this same guy's ears are still popping he the nerve to walk up to the foreman himself and ask him who it could be that is popping his ears with sophisticated electronic equipment. The foreman replied that is my poodle dog that is doing that to you to rate your ability here at work. The end.

Example 31 The Delusion Of Magic Power?

The delusion of magic power quite obviously would be that one thinks that one possesses magical power inside to any number of things including and especially- you guessed it, put hex's or curses on others that don' behave in the way that you wish that they would. Anyways I would guess that when they put the curse on the other guy that they think that they then resolved a problem of their own that way- got rid of the trouble right? Anyways, I for one do not believe that anyone that is a mortal human being has magic power inside of them to perform curses that really work. And if you think that you have such an outstanding ability I doubt that it's real. And if for some reason you would like to put a hex on me I say back hex, smecks! Get that one! There was really this guy though that really existed that thought that he had the power to hex his enemies and they would get in line with his wishes or they just might fall off. Anyways when he realized that his hex's on the other guy were not working then he became frustrated and though that he just might commit violence on his enemies that cross him. He was rational and civil though after all and would not stoop to this, but decided to just try new hex's on the other guy till the girl he loved came his way. The end, except to say that obviously to think one has magic power no matter who they are should be thought of as an absurd falsehood that has not been accurately proven, nor is it provable or real either one! In a word, delusion! A bazaar delusion as far as I am concerned!

Example 32 Delusion of Grandeur?

aturn

A delusion or grandeur is to believe that we are a deity, supernatural or famous person, perhaps here to fulfill a special purpose for man. They may think that they are Jesus Christ or Napolean for example. As with the last delusion discussed- "the delusion of magic power" these people quite often think that they have magic power.

There was this man that though he was Sparticus in a previous lifetime, and that every time that he comes back as a person God makes him a great liberator of people. He does not think that he has magic power, but charisma, charm wit, and honors having all of the virtues as much as he is capable of. He has a splendid personality! He has been sent to a doctor nonetheless to check him out over his apparent belief in reincarnation. The doctor for now is willing to testify that he believes that this same guy in question is really ok psychologically as long as he keeps his personal belief in reincarnation properly compartmentalized in proper relationship to his other beliefs. What it would take for this to be considered a delusion is just for one that you would have to prove overwhelmingly that this is not the case and no such proof exists one way or another to affirm or deny it's validity. The end!

aturn

Example 33 The Delusion of control

The delusion of control is the delusion that one' own thoughts are being controlled by someone other than your own self. First of all, as far wild as this may sound, there are apparently really people that believe this about themselves. They really do think that their thoughts are being controlled by a force beyond their own self. Everything from aliens from another planet controlling them, to the devil controlling them. Upon quick reflection about this particular delusion, one might think that it must be considered a bizarre delusion because you would think it lacks common sense reasoning that is fully rational, but believe it or not this particular kind of delusion could in certain circumstance be considered a non-bizarre delusion. Let me right here and now give you a ficticious example of where it could be said to be considered a non-bizarre one. There was this guy who said that he was getting shock treatment from the government where his ears popped. He thought that this same equipment that they had was somehow forcing him to choose

aturn

continued obsessive compulsive behavior that he know he ordinarily has better common sense than to act on it, but as of late got the better of him in that he gave into these compulsions over and over again! Now you can see how in this story there at least is some real logical thinking to it, so this example that I have just given you of the delusion of control should be considered non-bizarre believe it or not as far as my best judgement assesses! God bless the sick mentally! May their nerves heal as they grow into a more holistic picture of life and reality as fully normal and fully awake people experience it, in which we realize we have freewill, but are not confused about what we want in our choices!

Example 34 Delusion that someone of the opposite sex is in love with you – Erotomania!

According to Good Therapy, "Erotomania is a delusion that occurs when a person strongly believes-despite evidence to the contrary- that a person is in love with him or her." This of course means exactly that what it tells us: We may think that someone is in love with us even when better evidence to the contrary exists. Let me give you a aturn fictitious example to better illustrate what this delusion could be said to entail. When I was young about twenty yrs. old and worked in the bakery I met a female that worked at the same place that I did for a short time. From the day I met her I fell madly in love with her. Even though she was going steady with another guy I was just sure that she was the perfect person sanctioned from above for me to marry. Despite trying to make better friends with her she married this other guy while I continued on with a broken heart. I never believed to this day that she really loved this guy more than me, inspite of how this looked, but I reckoned her in-laws told her not to bother being my friend or romantically inclined with me on account of I was poor and her boyfriend's family was loaded with dough. Oh well I don't stalk her or bother her or anything like that but have tried to accept that she really wanted someone else more than me. Even though I have not seen her in years, but sometimes even now though on a cold winter night when I think about her I can still feel that same closeness that I felt as a young person better than 40 yrs. ago- and tell myself that I really know in my heart of hearts that she loves me just as much as I love her. The end!

aturn

Example 35 Delusion- From Living In The Past

It is very much the case that when people try to think and live their lives according to the way things used to be long after long they have now been thrust into a new situation where they should be bold enough to take on the "new" and face their present circumstances straight on with confidence and a good attitude for right now! Those old girl friends, old cars and old ways of doing things before computers can be out of touch to say the least. There was this guy that did not make the jump to computer literacy that he should have when the movement to computers for the general masses was on. He got a pretty good size social security check and pension also, so he could afford to buy a new computer and/or take a class that will make him what computer literate is for anything that he would wish to do with one. Now after several years since the computer invasion and revolution he still cannot do one think on a computer. He has no experience on a keyboard as he did not take typing in high school. And he can do none of the other functions on a computer. But of course it still obviously does not take that much learning to do many of the most basic functions on it. After bragging for ten years that he aturn could get by without a computer, he know regrets that he did not buy a computer and learn computer literacy. He is always running over to the neighbor's house or to a friend's house to look over his should on the computer to transact business that is vital that he participate in just to keep up with his life like he should. He was living in the past not keeping up with the new technology that is relevant for the times, telling himself he will keep the good old days when they are gone forever now like they were. He was believing a lie that common sense and good judgement should have told him otherwise. He is now finally getting a new computer and guess who he wants to help him learn how to use it. You guessed it my phone is now permanently off the hook! I'm joking of course! I'll be glad to show you how find your way around on the computer! That's why I'm here, I'll be that friend standing for you!

Example 36 Delusion From Misconstruing Cause and Effect- The Fallacy Of Post Hoc Ergo Proptor Hoc Fallacy

aturn

According to Wikipedia post hoc ergo propter hoc means: "Since event Y followed event X, event Y must have been caused by event X." (It is often shortened to simply post hoc fallacy.) What this translates into meaning is that because one event preceded another event, the one that happened first caused the second one to happen. An example of this kind of delusion or false assumption sometimes that can of course be related to the post hoc kind of reasoning is: Let's say your son that is by now full grown and not living with you anymore came over house to get the old football that was still in your closet. You know this to be the case because he called and said that he was coming over to get the football today, while you were at work. And when you got home it was gone. Also though you realized when you reached to take an aspirin that the whole bottle was missing. Your mind immediately races to the conclusion that your son must have done this because he was apparently over at the house earlier today. After throwing a fit in your own mind for a few minutes over this you realized that you left them in your bedroom from last night and forgot about it till right now. You have already tried and hung your son out in the sun for taking the bottle of aspirins with him in your imagination, but now your imagination turns out to be false! You have made a false assumption and delusion both. The reason that delusion fits even better than an assumption even is because even though you did not have direct evidence in front of you that it was not your son who did this but you knew that he had the reputation in front of everyone of never stealing anything from anybody, but always honest. So your assumption could be really considered a delusion too because not only what you thought to be the case turns out false, but knowing that your son's demeanor did not include theft would then give you by degree better proof that he probably did not steal your aspirin. A post hoc assumption or delusion either one could be said to be very dangerous, if one were to overact to what is not even the truth even though it may very much seem like it is! Let's be careful not make false assumptions or even be delusional based on post hoc reasoning but be aware of the possibility of this happening if we are to quick to jump to a false conclusion! Thank you!

Example 37 Demons or delusion?

aturn

When something goes wrong with people's behavior in that is now considered deviant or mentally ill either one the church even in 2019 claims that this is evidence of demon power. I for one am appalled by this convenient gimmick that in many cases is not helping any way. I believe that there is a rational way of understanding delusion that we are right now uncovering and how dare someone in the name of God or the devil either one tell us that it is demon power of all things. There was this young man that for two years in his early twenties had problems with his nerves where he was overly obsessive compulsive and did not trust other people enough sometimes to call it delusional thinking! Of the several times he attempted to get prayer from the prayer warriors at the local church they kept trying to cast the devil out of him, when he himself was sure that he had no devil at all in him, but was suspect he was just going thru a phase that hopefully he would grow out of. He quit being their personal friend because of this, but he did still like and believe in the general message of Christ that we all can turnaround: use our talents and learn to treat others with love and grow into enlightenment. He stayed positive about his illness and just kept seeing a doctor for his nerves in the meantime and took his medicine too. He by now not only does not need a counselor for aturn his nerves, because he is back in his right mind. He is by now too a fine community leader that preaches love for all, but cautions against anything that is not grounded in sound reasoning also.

Example 38 Delusion – The Invincibility Of The Professional Athlete

It undoubtedly take a lot of dedication and hard work to become a professional football player, basketball player or baseball player. It takes much diligence, perseverance and commitment too….! This is in itself a commendable achievement that we should not knock like praise for making excellence out of ourselves in this country! But now I maintain that there is an attitude that creeps up in the minds of many professional athletes that they are invincible, all-powerful, and always will be- that in some case makes them kind of haughty in terms of what they might think about the rest of us. Many of them think that the system is not anything that they should have to pay attention to at all because they are rich, famous, and perhaps very agile too.

aturn

Like because they think that they are young and strong in particular the most that they will always be that and the rest can just do what they want them to and everybody else is just there stepping stone! Like they are on a power trip! "Like Chow Mein man, you'll get in line behind me over how we use the law or politics or how we do anything else for that matter!" OK Bert Scoop played for the Pittsburg Steelers first string half back for several years. He was the best half-back in the NFL. He became corrupted by his money, strength and overall talent. He had developed a false sense of power where he thought that he could get away with drug peddling and pushing around those that did not like him personally as a result. He was living the delusion that he will always be young, rich, and strong and that whatever he wanted was automatically his! By the time he was fifty he had not given up illegal drug use, but was now broke living in a rundown apartment complex in Philadelphia. His wife had left him years before and said of him that he never accepted the aging process was real and then changed to a new and better attitude when it was time for him to do so- He never grew a heart for others like he should either! They found him dead laying on the floor of his apartment with heroine, cocaine and whiskey all three in him. The end!

aturn

Example 39 Delusion Or At Least Confusion Because We Lack enough Love And Full Maturity!

It is GW Hegel that said that that the "real is the rational" which is whew and amen kind of statement for obvious reasons. It is by sound reason alone that we understand properly anything that we are considering including the motives behind the behavior of others. To work for a government institution- namely the police department means that we look at things from the perspective of law, but time and life teach us too that we are really all in a different situation just trying to survive for the most part. In other words there is more to it then what an untrained person might catch to be 'fully competent police work" than what just anybody knows or realizes. But then they are sworn to uphold the law and if that means standing up to deviant behavior they do so. But then too there is the dimension of empathy or even compassion that sometimes comes into play while the police man is on duty. All of these things help go into the chemistry of what

aturn

makes a potentially good police officer. There was this rooky police officer that was having trouble on the job with inward turmoil that no one else knew about. He was beginning to develop a bad conscious as the job could sometimes get brutal even though he did not like this aspect of the job. He felt that at least sometimes he not paid attention perfectly to knowing who deserves a break more and who deserves incarceration. Why it was split second decisions in many cases, where he is a person in situation too coming from his new law and order job perspective. He went to the Penticostal church one Sunday morning just a few mile from his house. At the end of the sermon when the preacher asked anyone to step forward for prayer that needed it he immediately walked forward and shook a prayer warriors hand at the alter and then bowed his head and began to pray out-loud. He said, "Oh God I have taken on the responsibility to enforce law for a job that I really thought I would be enjoying. But so far it is not enough to just dish out the law to people. I want to love the people in my community even though there is obviously consequences for deviance and mistakes that we should not make. I want to be someone that loves everyone even with God's love inside. And Oh God I want all the virtues inside: the work ethic; honesty;

aturn patience; respect for human life; temperance; patience; and loving kindness. My conscience tells me that I should uphold the laws of Missouri for the sake of the people. But I want to incorporate more love in my heart for others and may you teach me wisdom in all ways amen! The people that were listening to him pray went wild with joy! The organist was playing in background "I Surrender All." Amen! The end!

Example 40 Delusion Of Power From Shooting A Gun

It is definitely true that overwhelmingly when someone shoots someone else, they shortly thereafter regret very much that they did this. For one most of time they have big jail time to serve for it and/or just because they realize and recognize no that it was a serious mistake to shoot this person anyways. I maintain that a bigger factor then people realize for why someone shoots an innocent person let's say it is because they wanted to feel a certain particular feeling of power potentially that it makes you feel like to shoot someone else

aturn

with a gun- you know like a power trip to shoot off a loaded pistol at someone. There was this guy named Barry Barchlow that used to love to target practice with a 38 Calibre Rossi that he owned with a permit for it, and also another permit to carry it with him to the shooting gallery. Now anyways even though this firearm that he practiced shooting all of the time at the shooting gallery was a small size weapon it still really made a pretty big bang when you shot it off! It gave him a false sense of power more than it should too. He had a little grudge against Kurt Anderson for stealing his women, when he needed her a lot more that Kurt did. Kurt had a lot more money and he was just thinking of his own personal passion for Katie and no one else when he stole her and then made her his wife. Kurt was a lot than Barry so to fight with Kurt with his fist over Katie was out. He wanted to get even so bad that he got his gun and shot Kurt right thru the heart with his Rossi. He had been imagining Kurt falling for one single fatal shot that he gave him which he did. Oh neato was just the feeling that he had when he shot him dead. He knew he'd be caught but just the thrill to get even with Kurt he decided to do. With blind passion and emotion as his guide he shot Kurt down dead. But now of course he was on his way to jail moments later. By the time he was

aturn

being fingerprinted at the jail he realized for sure that he had made big mistake. Not only would he have to go to jail for life if not get capital punishment which was not out as an option for this state, but he really had strong regret already for what he did. He now reasoned in his head that he should not have let his emotions rule his ability to reason ore sensibly then to commit such a horrific crime. He was sure in his mind also that if he hadn't been shooting off his Rossi a lot lately that apparently gave him a bigger power boost that he didn't realize before right this moment that got him in trouble. End of this story! ("Oh God I pray get a hold of people to get the help that they should when hurt emotionally by others before violence that ends up in tragedy happens. We all count so much and there are those that love and care about you so much and want you to be a winner without a runaway grudge against your neighbor! Amen!")

Example 41 Mood-Congruent Delusion

aturn

According to Wikipedia, "any delusion with content consistent with either a depressive or manic state." There was this guy that was depressed because of his lack of success as of late. In his mind he blames the state for making the law that which in his opinion caters to the pre-existing rich and leaves him out of opportunity. He thought people that have family members with good paying government jobs usually pass these jobs along to their children and the others are left out. That's why when he was school teacher for a short time he did not get promotion that he wanted to principal right away. This same guy was a professional rock-n-roller that when he finally got his big break in music he decide that this was a land of liberty, justice, and opportunity for all, after all.

Example 42 Mood Neutral Delusion

According to Wikipedia, "It is a delusion that does not relate to sufferer's emotional state." There was this guy that thought that people from Pluto would soon be dropping bombs from planet to ours. It never mattered whether this same guy was in a good or bad

aturn

mood, but in any frame of mind he still thought this even would happen any day now.

Example 43 Another Delusion of Persecution

Little Antebellum was 10 yrs. old when she decided that she wanted to be a professional dancer someday. At the ripe old age of 13 yrs. old she was taking lessons for dancing with real professional teachers at a nearby college that gave her dancing lessons at the expense of her mom. At the age of sixteen she was now as good as a professional dancer competing all over the state with her ability. She did not like two of her dance instructors because when they corrected her dancing ability they made comments of criticism that she took personally.   She almost quit and one point because she thought that one of them was too critical of her even when she danced flawlessly. The other one could be friendly or mean either one, but when you made a mistake she was meaner than what someone should have to put with. All in all this young female developed a persecution complex that did not fade quickly. By the time that she was twenty-five yrs. old she was one of the biggest dancers in that area of the country. One of

aturn

the same two people that looked over her should that could be mean sometimes was now still with her but they had much more friendlier encounters than how she once experienced it an earlier age. Her persecution complex by now had melted into solid friendships with as good as all of the people that taught her or danced with her. She now felt like an equal without a somewhat uphill climb battle with her responsibilities anymore. The mild inferiority complex that she had at a younger age went away totally. Praise God!

Example 44 Another Delusion Of Reference

There was this guy that everywhere he went at twenty-one years old he thought that others were teasing his head with secret messages to make him feel like he was not welcome or that he was not going to make the grade where he worked also. Like just as he pulled up for work one morning as he got out of the car he had the thought that he could be fired on this day for mistakes that were not mostly his own fault in his own department. Anyways just as he had this thought he looked over on the parking lot at a guy that smiled broadly at him but said nothing friendly to him. When he got inside of the building as he walked down the main aisle he had the thought that maybe he was not so welcome here anymore as he was just not welcome, a female walking the other way pinched he nose and looked right at him as if to say, "oh PU" when he knew he took a bath every day and did not think he needed a spiritual one either. Even though he did not lose his job all day they gave him hints, innuendos, insinuations that he was just not welcome or loved! Terrible of course!

    But now at twenty-five years old this same guy still worked at this same place and it was like a new heaven and earth to him by then. He had grown into a more positive friendly, and altogether stronger psychologically stable, person. And from the time that he walked thru the door to enter work every day there were smiles and "How you doing" from others. And all thru the day you were reinforced positive by other that you were love and welcomed. The mind games that people were playing to you were one of peace, love and friendship. Things went well at work as good as every day and almost everyone was your friend at work or wanted to be. You had gone thru a metamorphosis from twenty-one to twenty-five from a shy half backward guy to someone now tasting of the fruits of hard work and

aturn

enlightenment. The fear, the suspicion, the self-doubt had vanished and was now replaced with confidence and joy I like the words of an old pentecostal hymn that goes, "Lord lift me up and let me stand by faith on heaven's tabled land, a higher plane than I have found Lord plant my feet on higher ground!" Amen!

Example 45 The Delusion Of A Beyond If You Become Rich And Famous:

Kurt, who was a professional singer and piano player had always dreamed of meeting the big stars. He swore he was going to get good enough to play side by side with Barry Manilow on a piano. He swore he was going to sing somewhere while Elton John played the piano at the same time. He swore he would sing a duet with Stevie Knicks at a big concert too. Kurt, whereas he had only traveled sporadically, mostly in the same state or the one next to his, had always dreamed of traveling everywhere all over the country and make big money at it and know and be friends with the stars. He did not listen to most of

aturn

his best friends when they told him to pay attention to his finances the most if he make it big soon, that holding onto money was what was important and the glitter on the tree of the picture of the celebrity ball was just an arrangement of people and not a promise of continued success. To him though, in his imagination it would constitute a glamorous beyond that was full of fun and excitement with never-ending fun in it. When he finally got his new big break in music he was of course elated with joy. But when he finally got out on the road to make a bigger name for himself-and more money, he was astounded at how little he cared about the sights that he seen, or even meeting several of the stars in music except for a couple of them that he became long-term friends with. What surprised him the most is how little he liked eating in the fancy restaurants that were supposed to be so glamorous ad have the best food. Besides he was in a hurry all the time just to get in his practice and get set up for a show and of course to have good performance for the audience. He ended up eating at McDonalds most of the time on the road and it was a happy maker because it made him feel like he were back home again. The big money that he was supposed to get was heavily taxed and when it came to buying a new home in California all the big money was now aturn invested in it and he was even without cash sometimes. In the long run he moved back to where he came from originally in Iowa to cheapen his expenses to keep from filing bankruptcy. Anyways his glamorous picture of a fun beyond turned out not to be the case-you might call it a delusion of naivety-even though he know a lot of facts about each state that were positive. He was believing a lie if he told himself that there was a glamorous beyond when in fact it was just his singing career itself and the money that he made that he did hold onto that counted out of it.

Example 46 The Delusion That Money Means Happiness

Timothy Winthrop thought that if he just got rich that would make him happy. He was told by countless people that blind ambition without a heart makes for a sad person if even when they get their hands on the dough! Well he worked hard for his company on the business management side and made it all the way to CEO before forty yrs. of age. He had a wife and family that he loved and provided for,

aturn

even though it took some sacrificing along the way with how he spent money in order to make it big. The kids did not get an allowance but only presents that included money sometimes at Christmas or their birthday, even though their education clothes and small amounts of money to go out with on the weekend were sometimes allotted to them. The new house that he thought that he might buy had to wait. He was thirty eight till he actually moved from a house that he wanted to move from at 29 yrs. of age. His wife worked as a supervisor in the same plant and had more money for expenses and the family in general this way. They wanted a dog, but decided that he would be too much of a nuisance and expense to them. But now just before forty yrs. old he was promoted to CEO of the company. Can you imagine that? Well anyways money miracles do happen sometimes and his promotion to CEO was one of them. A short time later his wife decided that she wanted a divorce, but after trip to their favorite restaurant where they ate, drank, and danced together, and also he apologized for neglecting her and the kids so much for the job they reconciled. They now would be better friends again for the rest of his life. As far as the job as CEO went he could not continue to keep up

aturn

with all of its demands, and keep the wife happy and spend time with the kids to develop their character like he wanted to so he voluntarily went back to the executive position that he had before this one. He was happier and more fulfilled in the long-run because of it. The End!

Example 47 A Religious Delusion That she Didn't Fall For

Laura Baker was a young Amish girl that wanted to date a new guy at 18 yrs. of age. From her parents and the head Reverend from the church she was not supposed to take her hair down on a date but keep it pinned up with a white cap on it. Well she was now getting tired of what she by now thought to be religious repression from her parents and the church that she reluctantly still attended. She now thought of it as a lie and border line delusional thinking. She still believed in the doctrine of Salvation-that we could be born again of a Big love for everyone inside that should leads us to actions full of love and goodness. But she by now was doubting many of the church doctrines that were blocking or hindering at least what she was trying

aturn

to do. She told herself that her future would have to be for happiness sake with a young man was sensible and hip like she is that is believing that it is bad or evil to let your hair down. She by now is married to this same guy and the go to the Baptist church together every Sunday of the world with their two children. She drives a car, wears her hair down 90% of the time, and also wears make-up every day. She still believes in the deity of God's Son- Jesus Christ, and follows the general moral and ethical pathway to heaven by being good in a genuine sense of what she knows that to be, but does not worry about trite doctrines that are outdated that thwart the pursuit of happiness and turn people off to the Savior as far as she is concerned. The end!

Example 48 The Delusion Of Taking It Personally

From the time he was child this guy took everything personally. I mean to the degree that he had a common sense problem or confusion with reality in that he told himself the lie that it was better to overact and write off, and not be a friend anymore to someone that criticized him or disagreed with him about whatever, or over mild rejection in general. His first girl friend at 18 yrs. old did not marry

aturn

him because he would not brush his teeth enough. When she told him that he should brush his teeth more he was insulted personally to the point that he dumped her instead over the confrontation. He was an ace basketball player and somehow won a scholarship to play college basketball, but when the coach pushed him verbally to perform at his best he simply went into a rage and quit the team altogether. At work fifteen yrs. later he almost won employee of the month, but that mean't shaking the members of management's non-union supervisors, which to him was treason against the union principle. He gave up a $500 dollar bonus because of his decision right then and there. Before he passed away he asked to be cremated even though in his heart of hearts he really wanted his corpse preserved with an open casket funeral, but since a small minority of the family members said they didn't like him he decided that his body should be cremated with no funeral at all. I think that it is safe to say that this guy overacted along the way to better possibility, and if he had not done so he would have been a much bigger success! Heaven help us all!

Example 49 Is Salvation Delusion Or Help For It?

aturn

    Rebecca used to cry a lot as a small child over little things that bothered her, but by five she was much improved and was ready to begin kindergarten with the other children the same age. By the time she was sixteen she was the valedictorian of her school. Her parents believed in God very much but Rebecca was thinking that an intellectual understanding or what good was supposed to be- morals and ethics was all there was or is to religion. Rebecca did well in school from here thru the first year of college, but after that she began to have nervous breakdown and almost had to pull out of school till she got better. She could no longer focus like she did and was fearful that even if she recovered from this in time she would over-looked because she is a female and not a male. She just plain was believing that now at her tender age it was all about to end for her probably soon, when it was really only the beginning. He friend invited her to a Pentecostal church meeting while this was going on. On intuition she went to the meeting and listened to a preacher that said that if we are Born Again with God's Love inside that we will be sustained thru every crisis. At the end of the sermon she went forward to choose

aturn

incorporating Love inside. It turned out that not enough Love in her heart for everyone was what the problem. She was never a bigot or the likes of that, but she needed more love in her heart in everyday life for confidence and success. Well within a few weeks she was coming out of her almost paranoid corner inside of herself to a bolder and more confident person again- not only with the school work itself, but in all that she did including socialize with her friends when in order. She was now a true believer in the idea of Love from God inside being relevant for everyone! Instead of just knowing with a partial intellectual understanding of God, she was now walking with Love inside! She became very successful as a writer. Her faith in a Big Love changed her for the rest of her life and she even wrote one enormous best-seller book on the rights of women. She was invited to give a speech before the women for Christ at Harvard University and the last thing she said to them was it was not till the realization of Supernatural Love for everyone came inside me that I gained the true confidence that I should have in front of everyone.

Example 50 Postal Schizophrenia

aturn

There was this man that had postal schizophrenia, in that he believed that he would not get his mail sometimes even when he had never harassed the mail man or hindered the mail to anyone in any way. As of late he had a bitch with the government about taxation, but this had nothing of course to do with his mail it's just that he thought at least that this would make the entire US government react to his perspective on taxation so that he would not get his mail. He realized deep down inside that this this was not rational enough to believe in light of common sense, even if it had an obvious logic to it.

It was a Wednesday and he was supposed to be getting a check from a relative in the mail on this day, but yet he was fearful that his mail would just not come and that maybe it never would again. Anyways low and behold to his great surprise positively his check did come in the mail on this day! From then on he told himself that he would not fear his mail not being sent to him again when there was really every reason to believe that it was coming. He was proud of the fact that he had never said anything harrassful to the mailman nor did any other thing to hinder the mail. He was also proud of the fact that he always been polite altogether and friendly to the mailman... even offering him a bottle of cold water on a hot day. He told himself that

aturn

from now on he was not going to let ludicrous fear overshadow his ability to be stay fully rational in what he believed to be the case! He still get his mail by now- even more checks in the mail sometimes! If you have postal schizophrenia yourself unless you harassed the mailman or otherwise hindered what he was doing you should feel confident that you are going to get your mail. Rain, sleet or snow the US mail will get there! Stay civil and you will get your mail if they have any to deliver to you!

Example 51 Oh That Family!

Herb was a great child. He ate everything on his plate at supper and was honest and followed the Golden Rule in how he treated others. He liked his friends at church well enough and had respect for everybody including the preacher. But now Herb was still different from his mom who raised him or his siblings that were going to stay an insider to organized religion all of their adult life, with one of them becoming a preacher. Herb liked natural rock-n-roll music and cold beer too when he got old enough to drink it but was good to everybody- quite virtuous! He did indeed dance to the beat of a aturn different drum though as he became a professional rock singer and even joined a band. Entertainment of the natural kind was his thing. He loved goodness, but to him that mean't the priority values of work, honesty and love for all, and not church doctrines against rock music, beer, and long hair. Now the rest of the family picked on him for his lack of piousness and commitment towards the institution of the church! When he went thru a crisis with alcohol for a short time they all yelled at him that this was sign of demon possession and indecency altogether! When he cut his first rock CD the family said he was going to hell for gambling with God's money and blasphemy too. They tried to put him away for shaming the family culture- they said he was delusional in that he lived in a rock fantasy, and too was harmful for America when it was obviously not true. He was by this time a stable enough person by this time, and had plenty of friends to vouch for his sanity, so it did not work! He learned not to hate God or goodness because he disagreed with his family about a particular lifestyle that was full of church doctrine and commandments of men, but did really know what it mean't to love others and show it with his actions every day! He cut a hit song eventually that was about brotherly love for everyone that saved a lot of young people from hate and disaster! His

aturn

life was a good work after all! He was not about to run from entertainment when it was in his blood, intuition, and even conscience to entertain others in such a way! He also eventually became a community leader and change his mind about AA! His realization was that AA indeed saved millions of lives from serious alcohol dependency whether you personally believe in drinking in moderation or to abstain from alcohol altogether up the road! His life was a blessing to all even though he worked outside the literal church full of doctrines that he apparently didn't like or need! Be good though! The end!

Example 52 The Delusion to Misconstrue Cause And Effect

Now in example 37 of different kinds of delusions I talk about the misconstruction of the truth by mistaking that because one event preceded another that the first also caused the second to happen. This of course is referred to the Post Hoc Ergo Propter Hoc Fallacy. But now in this particular example of how someone mistook cause and

aturn

effect it is not just because the first event may have preceded in time the second to happen, but just that indeed you attribute something to be caused by something else even when we may have at least known initially that something else caused it. An example of this kind of delusion would be if we were chewed out at work for not doing a job right. Well instead of accepting responsibility for what happened you decided to name other indirect potential factors for why you have not in general been able to keep them happy with your work. Initially you knew exactly why you failed to do the job right that the pointed out to you, but you decided to rationalize other things related. And then in the long run when you recount this story you actually begin to believe this rationalization that you have made up even though you knew otherwise and half forget what the biggest cause was. When you really by now believe your own alibi and rationalization that does not really explain in the best way what exactly happened instead of the most pertinent direct cause then you have succeeded in becoming delusional by definition. Keep up with what your conscience tells you!

aturn

Example 53 Reading The Signs –(A Delusion Of Reference)

Poor Bertrand, every time he looked around seen what were like signs in the behavior of others or just a symbolic meaning coming alive to even dead matter that could be manipulated by man that reflect a special meaning to him. These were negative signs in the behavior itself right in front of you by other people. These were sings with a negative message to them that promoted paranoia, fear, doubt, suspicion, and a general mistrust in him for others. He also experienced signs in the behavior of others that made him feel like that he was not needed to share with others what he had to contribute with his work, and that he was just welcome to hang out with the happy troops of labor. Altogether he felt hated and rejected! For example at work when he got there almost no one was ever friendly to him, but it was all just a tug of war with the work without any positive relationships with others on the job. People always starred at him that implied the meaning "I don't know about you." When he would strike up a conversation with others about anything besides work-related communication they did not pay any mind to

aturn

what he had to say. When they corrected him for an occasional on the job mistake they were really mean and short with hm. Altogether it seemed like many if not most of the people that he worked with day-by day were also showed signs of rejecting everything about him, and wishing him ill-fate up the road. These people seemed to him to just not have any love or understanding in their heart for him at all!

Bertrand however was smart enough to not give up and eventually things began to change for the better. In the meantime he started going to church and even a Bible study to feed his new faith that love could be had for everyone including not just himself but others too! Yes according to the Christian faith we are to love one another and that was what we missing in his life. From now on he wanted to continue to work as hard as he could and show real love for others in everyday life situations which won him more personal success!

Finally he now begin to experience being liked by practically everyone and the signs in other behavior so to speak for "hi" were signs of approval and respect for him! What do you know- the world is as we are- if we are positive and friendly enough than we should be able

aturn

to get along better with others! Love is reciprocal! Thank God for "good vibrations" with others and happy days!

Example 54 A Persecution Delusion

    A persecution delusion exists when someone thinks that right from the start people are to get them or hurt them in some way deliberately when it is just not the case. As I have already stated a persecution delusion in many cases if not most overlaps with a persecution complex or a persecution delusion moreover. In the last example just given of a persecution that constitutes a delusion of reference, but it could very well be and underlying delusion of persecution too that this person has at the same time. Poor Alfred was mistreated by his step parents as a child and unfortunately it apparently affected how he understood the meaning of the behavior of others to think that that just like his step parents that they were out to get him in one way or another. That's right he really thought aturn because of the bad experiences he had with his step parents that in the world at large there were actual conspiracies by other people out there too. The rest of the crew never talked to him very much when he first started where he was at and Alfred seen this as an indication that they were really against him and did not want him to succeed. In time though Alfred gained the respect from his co-workers that he should have by working hard and treating others good like you should on the job. When Alfred really began to get good on the job and had succeeded in finding many friends also the persecution delusion that he started out with when he began to work there vanished. What do you know- when you can see eye to eye with others about how to go about work a persecution delusion will just plain melt away! Even when in many cases someone was abused by others at a young age they can still transcend how this has hindered their personality since they were a kid! A persecution delusion can be healed-especially with the willingness to keep trying with a good attitude!

aturn

Example 55 Getting Out of The Boat- (A parallel comparison Between Jesus Christ And Jean Paul Sartre Philosophy)

Rarely have I heard of a comparison between Jesus Christ and Jean Paul Sartre, but I know they really in some sense wanted to do the same thing: and that is challenge the young people to get out of the boat so to speak and learn values on your own to a large degree, making themselves a winner by becoming a professional in whatever field of learning that they chose. In a culture with strictly the view of the Jewish nation, Jesus radicalized a new Philosophy that was based more on love and forgiveness than the law of the Old Testament itself, all by itself. When Peter got out of the boat and attempted to come to Jesus this of course symbolizes moving closer to the ideals of Christ and that is to incorporate the Love of God inside and also have a Big love in our heart for others that includes using our talents. Jesus did not put any emphasis on the law all by itself like "how to go about being a winner by adding love inside including using our talents too." And then shining your positive light-including the knowledge that we learned by using our abilities that includes education even unto

aturn

professionalism in many cases. Jesus said in effect that we should be help in whatever field of learning that we are inspired from above to be in. And He had care for everyone no matter where they came from. In the story of The Good Samaritan. He said that it is not nation against nation, but instead the war was with the potential darkness of our own mind, related to how we treat others. We are to love others and make a kingdom of heaven, God- Love right here on earth with the willingness to change the world for the better by using our God given abilities with a heart for all!

Jean Paul Sartre, one of the most celebrated existentialist thinkers of the 19th century, too had relevant ideas on the topic of values. Sartre wanted us to know that we are very much on our own in terms of what values we will choose to have over the course of the rest of our life. He tells us that it is "anguish" the experience of having to make decisions on our own as a young adult. We must learn to decide what values we will choose for ourselves, but that there are consequences for any and all action that we take! He was honestly getting around to seeing something important. One should easily see how one could steer themselves upward with greatness in the making with good choices then about how to live…. Sartre said if we trust

aturn

what we should not, instead of a pathway that we should trust then we are acting with "bad faith" as he calls it because we are choosing that which is not to be trusted in the light of good sense. If we chose to have sex and get a female pregnant when it is not expedient for your personal career at this time and under the particular circumstances that you did this under, then a bad choice maker might be what someone may think of you then. So the bottom line for Sartre is that even though we may have much freedom to choose our own future it is still smart to be wise instead of not wise in what we choose.

    Now I know that Jesus and Sartre wanted us to get out of the boat of complacency and bad judgement to learn walk on the Waters of Life by the positive plight of the values we develop. Well, what does this have to do with delusion? A constructive person that makes wise choices we should revere as a means to help us become stable and help us to rise above potential delusion along the way by getting out of the boat and learn from a life more of self-reliance but don't forget Good, or good choices!

Example 56 Taking Care of Business!

aturn

There is almost nothing that is as exhilarating or as confidence boosting, but sometimes frustrating, as learning to be competent just in handling your own personal finances. At one time as kids of course, almost without exception, we did not have to take care of the overall household expenses like paying the rent, house payment, utilities and potentially property taxes, groceries, gas for the automobile, clothes, and whatever other routine household expenses that we incur. Nor do they pay out of their own pocket for health care or emergencies in health care or whatever else other than that constitutes an emergency situation that involves directly or indirectly the children.

But then as young adults out on your own you will have to learn to take care of all your household expenses all by yourself aside possible help from your parents still or government assistance. We need to learn in a hurry to pay on time all of the bills as they come in on time to keep in a house or apartment with working utilities, gas for the car, groceries and clothes. Medical care and dental too, in which insurance may not cover all of.

AS a young adult we could almost get an ulcer, a panic attack because it may sometimes not be easy to cover consistently all of the household expenses that we incur. Our first full-time job out in the

aturn

real world as a young adult simply may not make a lot of money, in fact it may leave us way below the poverty line. Working an extra part-time job additionally might be helpful if we can keep it up for long and still do our other job plus the part-time job that we have in acceptable fashion enough to please the boss! But now one of the questions that goes thru a young person's mind as a young adult may be for many of them when in the world are they going to be able to make enough money to pay the bills up consistently and have enough money left over for ourselves for groceries that are tasty or for pleasure in general. That's right when in the world are they going to be able to get a chance to splurge a check and have some real fun with it- like take a trip somewhere to vacation and/ or visit friends, or have a hot date with the opposite sex let's say for instance where we really wine and dine it up or dance till midnight. They are caught up in just paying the bill like they have for the time being sometimes if they are going to stay into their house with heat in it and food to eat etc.

As we go along we may finally find a job that pays well enough not to live below the poverty line and we may finally even have savings for a change, and even enough time for more simple pleasure in our own free time. At least sometimes this really happens for us!

aturn

So now where or how does the idea of delusion come into play, while we learning to handle all of our household expenses. Well now it is indeed difficult sometimes to bear poverty at a young adult age or any time in our life for that matter. One in this situation could think that the system is automatically against them, when this may not be the case. This then can be considered delusion or delusional sometimes, when it is just not the case. The truth is instead that you may definitely need a college education for. Restaurant work does usually not pay very high wages. The assembly line worker in manufacturing is slowly being replaced by robots and more automation in general. In order to work with computers you need college education. Jobs in education as a teacher definitely require a college education. Service oriented jobs in particular in medicine, whether it is a doctor even just an RN require higher education. Even in many jobs in security and law enforcement my too require at least higher education of a master's degree in order to qualify for many of the jobs in this field. Altogether our society has quickly gone thru a transition where one definitely need higher education in technology or the humanities and social sciences to be competent enough to acquire a higher paying job. This is reality and a fact, so one had better

aturn

consider as a young person staying in school a few more years after high school to get more education at a higher level yet.

Example 57 Taking Care Of Business! Part II!

　　Now at some point in our life especially after the early years of our adult life where we for a short time may be struggling learning how to make more and also how to budget it, actually succeed in really doing just that. And whereas it may have been a major difficulty just a short time ago to keep the bills paid, we now have money to save or splurge when we need a vacation or buy something nice. We are now entering a new phase in our ability to acquire and handle money that changes our life for potentially more fun and fulfillment at the same time.

　　Now if we are smart of course even at this new juncture in our ability to make money, we will at the same time learn to be more frugal, and save and/or invest in that which lead us to more total assets. The time is now to make your money and use it wisely not only for a better house or car, but to get set up with a whole portfolio of stocks, bonds, and other savings and security measures for you future aturn and the future of your children. It is time to inherit what begins to feel like your share of the pot of money on this earth! You should too begin to feel like an economic success for a change-oh that feels good! You may even begin to feel the feeling of power that comes from money if we make enough of it and have plenty of assets including potential ownership of a business! After all we are now successful and this at least just might make you feel like you are reaping better rewards and more fulfillment even though it is not a guarantee in itself of complete continued happiness as a result.

So what is the delusion that befalls someone that is aspiring like this economically? Well just a sense of power that you think is permanent turns out to be temporary as a good paying job sometimes goes away as a results sometimes get eliminated and thriving business that you may own make go belly up some time unexpectedly. Economic success usually has its ups and downs both and is just one big jolly joy ride. It is love that remains that you have in your heart for others and not just the possibility of money –that is what is most real!

Example 58 Staying Up With It

There of course have been more nervous breakdowns for those just trying to stay up with their life: Their work for survival sake and

aturn

additionally just keeping up with keeping the house clean and handling the literal work it takes to keep track of and manage any bills to be paid.

    Staying up with our job that we do for a living of course comes first before anything else or we would not be able to pay the bills- at least that is true for the overwhelming amount of people that are still at a young enough age to be in the job market of today. For all of us just learning to keep up with the demands of a new job while we are still learning the job itself can sometimes be challenging if not difficult for us. Then too if we are going thru a crisis of one sort another in our life while on the job it may make it difficult to keep up even as a result just for one. Then too add all of the chores and housekeeping that we do have to keep up with at home can add up to a lot of work-many many hours of work in fact. There is a tremendous book by Juliet Shore called The Overworked American in which she tells how it is the case that people actually spend more time just keeping the house clean that includes doing the laundry than what one might realize which then leaves them with very little free time for themselves. All in all one could be plagues by nervous exhaustion or a mild nervous breakdown as a result. When in the world if we are working a job

aturn

where we must work a lot of hours and then go home and clean the house too we could go into shock from and really, really need a break! One can be more proned to being burned out as a result.

The delusion that comes into play from all this kind of effort could render the feeling that one is just a slave or commodity because one is spending so much time with work! One could feel like just a machine instead of a person that deserves so much more! Do of course find a way to make more free time for yourself no matter when all the work just starts pulling at your wits. We all have to learn to find the necessary time to rest up foremost. I feel like life is not worth living unless we can find a way to make it a pleasant experience.

Example 59 The Fast-Lane

We live in the fast-paced world in the modern era like never before. If you go out on the free-way to work in a big town like Chicago or Indianapolis you really might be confronted with a lot of traffic in the hurry where you really have to know how to drive a car if you going be live. The words "merge" and "speed" come to mind!

aturn

At work the same thing happens! It's all a hurry, hurry, hurry, rat race to get things done! If let's say your work to the assembly line in a factory you are almost always expected to really get the parts out like your job was to drive the Indy 500! And if you were to work in the office of this same plant you would be challenged with the demands of getting work done in the office that includes real diligence, perseverance and commitment consistently day after day!

And then when you go to the supermarket later on this same day- at the checkout lane it too is a very hurried ordeal! Put you items down quickly out of your cart! Get out your savings card for that store! Hurry to install your debit or credit card to pay for the purchase if you don't have cash on you! Then hurry grab your bags quick as the person behind you in this same line wants service too! Go, go, hurry, hurry! And then hurry out the door of the store with your purchase and literally race to your car!

When you finally sit down in the evening and recount the day you might have some positive memories of the day, but you just might occasionally question to yourself all of the hurrying that you did!

All of the time a young person in their early twenties may have bit off more than they can chew and they feel like they are going crazy

aturn

from stress, when if they just stopped and analyzed the pace that modern society forces you to do things no wonder it makes you occasionally feel like you're going batty from stress! And like they think they are having a total nervous breakdown sometimes, when they just need to know themselves better in relationship to their situation and know to take it easy when they should! It is delusion to blame yourself for the pace that the modern world impresses upon us and along with that think you are going mad for good when again you just need to take it easy! Let's learn to take it easy when we can and should, and none of us were just made to be a speed machine all of the time and never human being too. What happened to a world where people were friendly and loved each other? What's wrong with Dolly Parton or President Jimmy Carter just happening to be in the checkout lane at the supermarket making the whole room turn their head and smile as they share a friendly and potentially amusing moment with the check- out clerk! Let me tell you something ladies and gentlemen this world is going to perish unless we put enough love in it! Let's be a friend to others realizing we are not made to just hurry like a machine, but to love and dig each other too!

aturn

Example 60 Individual Rights Vs. The Collective Good Of The Society:

In America, we are committed to individual rights in our society much more than in another country like China or North Korea. It is of course established in our constitution of the United States in the bill of rights that has been a guide for how we view law and ultimately how we then treat people. The first amendment in the bill of rights says:

Preamble

Congress of the United States begun and held at the City of New-York, on Wednesday the fourth of March, one thousand seven hundred and eighty nine.

THE Conventions of a number of the States, having at the time of their adopting the Constitution, expressed a desire, in order to prevent misconstruction or abuse of its powers, that further declaratory and restrictive clauses should be added: And as extending the ground of public confidence in the Government, will best ensure the beneficent ends of its institution.

RESOLVED by the Senate and House of Representatives of the United States of America, in Congress assembled, two thirds of both Houses concurring, that the following Articles be proposed to the Legislatures of the several States, as amendments to the Constitution of the United States, all, or any of which Articles, when ratified by three fourths of the said Legislatures, to be valid to all intents and purposes, as part of the said Constitution; viz.

aturn

ARTICLES in addition to, and Amendment of the Constitution of the United States of America, proposed by Congress, and ratified by the Legislatures of the several States, pursuant to the fifth Article of the original Constitution.

Photo: Gilbert Stuart via Wikimedia Commons

Thomas Jefferson wrote to James Madison advocating a Bill of Rights: "Half a loaf is better than no bread. If we cannot secure all our rights, let us secure what we can."

First Amendment

Congress shall make no law respecting an establishment of religion, or prohibiting the free exercise thereof; or abridging the freedom of speech, or of the press, or the right of the people peaceably to assemble, and to petition the Government for a redress of grievances.

Second Amendment

A well regulated Militia, being necessary to the security of a free State, the right of the people to keep and bear Arms, shall not be infringed.

Third Amendment

No Soldier shall, in time of peace be quartered in any house, without the consent of the Owner; nor in time of war, but in a manner to be prescribed by law.

Fourth Amendment

The right of the people to be secure in their persons, houses, papers, and effects, against unreasonable searches and seizures, shall not be violated, and no Warrants shall issue, but upon probable cause, supported by Oath or affirmation, and particularly describing the place to be searched, and the persons or things to be seized.

Fifth Amendment

No person shall be held to answer for a capital, or otherwise infamous crime, unless on a presentment or indictment of a Grand Jury, except in cases arising in the land or naval forces, or in the Militia, when in actual service in time of War or public danger; nor shall any person be subject for the same offence to be twice put in jeopardy of life or limb; nor shall be compelled in any criminal case to be a witness against himself; nor be deprived of life, liberty, or property, without due process of law; nor shall private property be taken for public use without just compensation.

aturn

Sixth Amendment

In all criminal prosecutions, the accused shall enjoy the right to a speedy and public trial, by an impartial jury of the State and district wherein the crime shall have been committed; which district shall have been previously ascertained by law, and to be informed of the nature and cause of the accusation; to be confronted with the witnesses against him; to have compulsory process for obtaining witnesses in his favor; and to have the assistance of counsel for his defence.

Seventh Amendment

In Suits at common law, where the value in controversy shall exceed twenty dollars, the right of trial by jury shall be preserved, and no fact tried by a jury shall be otherwise reexamined in any Court of the United States, than according to the rules of common law.

Eighth Amendment

Excessive bail shall not be required, nor excessive fines imposed, nor cruel and unusual punishments inflicted.

Ninth Amendment

The enumeration in the Constitution of certain rights shall not be construed to deny or disparage others retained by the people.

Tenth Amendment

The powers not delegated to the United States by the Constitution, nor prohibited by it to the States, are reserved to the States respectively, or to the people. (ACLU)

We pride ourselves here in this country especially that we have the

right of freedom of speech and of the press and of religion. We brag

aturn

that we can own a gun too. We are glad that we have due process of law too! These kinds of rights are not necessarily present in many, many other countries. Our system is not perfect, but we do very much believe in individual rights!

    Now over on the other side of the coin is "what can be seen for the collective good of us all- including our concern for everyone to be safe and their property and rights are protected as well as our reputation to the degree it should be protected. Well now this makes a point too that is very important and relevant to us all every second. It is our right to speak our mind freely, but when we deliberately are lying about or slandering someone else we have violated others rights. It may be our right to have a drink too, but to violate safety in the road is not our right. To protest is our right when we have a permit and it is non-violent. It is not our right to riot and loot though when one is protesting though. What if everyone else when they didn't get their way in court on day one went out and rioted and looted against innocent people. And everyone deserves their day in court no matter who they are or what they may have done. We want to know of course what all of the relevant information about what happened. It is our right to have religious freedom but when our religion says that we kill innocent people or that we neglect sick children so that they do not get necessary medical help when they need we are violating the rights of the innocent!

So now who is right- the side that says that stresses the most we need individual rights or the side that say the collective good of us all is important, especially when it concerns the safety of us all? Well now quite obviously we need both individual rights, but at the same time law that forbids unsafe and unfair practices! This double-edged sword though we must keep in mind though as we need both sides in the issue. Individual right should not supersede all our safety including our life, property and reputation. On the other hand we want freedom to reign as much as possible?

As this double-edged sword goes who is delusion, or believing a falsehood that is outside of reality? Well this of course could go either way, but we definitely need both for freedom for us all, but with it comes responsibility if we are going to be safe honest, and fair towards others! You can believe what you want basically in religion but you cannot violate the safety and welfare of a child that needs medical assistance. We can get permission to protest non-violently, but to jeopardize other people's rights in the process is out! To have a

aturn

drink may be permitted, but to jeopardize the safety of us all with your habit we will not permit!

We should be glad that we have individual rights to a big degree in this country, but remember always once again that with freedom comes responsibility as safety is not a joke! God Bless you.

Example 61 Who's The Toughest?

Well now when I say who is the toughest in the context I am about to allude to I am not referring to who is the toughest all of the way around as in how physical fit one might be in itself or the psychological strength of someone either, but who in the small would be able to win in an all physical confrontation against someone else.

I think that is quite normal to have the instinct of self-preservation where one at least measures up in their mind so to speak whether they could defend themselves in a fight against whoever else or perhaps even more than one person at one time to fight. I do not mean by that, that you are looking for a fight but just wondering with the instinct of self-preservation whether you could defend yourself if you had to against one or more people that do not play by the rules, in

aturn

that they start a fight with someone else instead of being civil and a gentleman.

    Anyways the actual point that I am trying to make by bringing up this topic is that some people live in a fantasy world about how tough they think they might be, when they are really kidding about or exaggerating how strong that they actually are. Consider the scenario of someone going in the bar for a drink or two and then after each one that he actually has he keeps getting tougher in his own estimation. He tells himself that with just one more shot of whiskey in him that he could waup the biggest guy in the room. Well of course now he is feeding himself a line of shit by this point and he has no point to really make with his fist at all! It makes no sense in the first place to go to the well with fist fighting as it is very dangerous in very many ways, and a better man would stay civil and call the bar-tender over to his table if someone was so drunk that they wanted to start an uncalled for fight with him. One tie I was sitting in the restaurant/ bar about to sing the next karaoke song. Well this guy made bee line towards my table and said that he wanted to get it on with his fist with me. I pointed to the biggest guy in the room and said well now he looks like someone that might be able to fight with you. The guy got frustrated

aturn

and left me alone. Oh for goodness sake just call the bartender over if you got a problem with some head-case fighter! Stay civil as the consequences of fighting can be pretty steep sometimes! And yes it takes a real big man to fight with someone just because they think they are bigger! Let's not be that way!

And oh it can definitely be considered delusion that one thinks one is tough enough to waup everybody else when it isn't even true in the first place. And now alcohol in excess is atrocious and violence is not the answer, but peace love and civility! Know when to say when with alcohol! God Bless you!

Example 62 Do I Love Everybody Enough?

If the name of the game is to stay positive to win then it pays to put a little bit of love in your heart towards others like we should have. That's right if we can just stay in love with others it makes it a little bit easier to treat them good too. Nobody just always is in there very best mood every single minute but if we think positively about how we feel about other people with love and appreciation for them this should help us to overcome a lack of co-operation from others in working together on whatever. People that treat others with love usually have more friends too and can glide over problems that someone else may not.

And then what does it mean to love others simply because you just do, and are expecting nothing in return, but even then love brings joy and happiness to the person that rendered it. God honors the love in our hearts for each other. Jesus said to love one another even as I have loved you. Agape love and altruism we should revere and strive towards! Old fashioned love should abound on this earth and then we should always get along well enough to keep the planet rolling along well enough for people to survive and be happy.

So now where could delusion come into play in this scenario? Well to be honest it is really when we have no love for others that we are more likely to be delusional has been assessment. It is when we are just too stubborn to love just anybody in everyday life that we have un-necessary clashes and fall away with them. Love even covers a multitude of sins says the Bible. And finally might I remind you of a line in a carol King song where she says "only love is a reason and everything else is illusion." Let's keep on loving others like we should

aturn

and make this a beautiful place to live down here on earth. Finally let me allude to the words of a REO song that I like. It says, I'm going to keep on loving you because it's the only thing I want to do-I don't want to eat I don't want to sleep I just want to keep on loving you.!"
God Bless You

Example 63 Unconditional Acceptance

Now in everyday life situations I try not to make too many value judgement as it pertains to the appearance of another or the lifestyle that one lives either one. I believe in tolerance and goodwill in how I judge people right of the top of my head. Well now but if it is my own family or a close friend I might pull them aside and tell them that they can do better if they act a little bit smarter. A guy at work that was older than me once said to me while on the job, "if you settle for a little Johnson you will never get a lot." Well to me by now this makes a lot of sense and inadvertently it is true that I made no major commitments to bar my future in entertainment! Isn't nice when aturn someone out of love and not hate or jealousy routes for you to do better.

Well now where does the concept of delusion come into play where we are believing a falsehood about whatever when we should know better than that? Well believe it or not I am going to conjecture that those who will not accept constructive criticism when it is in order stay in a smaller world that is nearly exciting as being a bigger winner. And at least sometimes it reflects delusion about what motivated someone to try and get you to do better for yourself with constructive criticism. People are not always against you just because they would tell you to improve and make your life better. This is no evil necessarily, but in most case it could be a best friend that truly wants you to do better in the long run! God Bless! Get out of the boat and make yourself a bigger winner!

Example 64 A Double Standard

Now as it pertains to a double-standard in anything the first thing that someone might be inclined to say back is big story of how it is the

aturn

case when and where in their life that they were discriminated against. That's right they are going to tell you about how they were people turned away simply because they were not rich or poor enough to fit appropriately. I myself am glad for the coming day of civil rights for us all, especially the poor-and with every skin color or whatever walk of life. Rich and poor you know can be discriminated against and both sexes and all ages can experience it. I thank God for Martin Luther King, and LBJ in making the possibility for the poor side of town to have the unheard of opportunity of going to college or university! A new day was dawning in America! I still remember when Jesse started the Rainbow Coalition He promised that civil right extended to all of the poor and not just blacks! A whole new world with higher education for all of those who really wanted to get one was now a reality! Mass ignorance in so many ways was now becoming a thing of the past.

Now in reality discrimination and double standard of one or another still goes on to virtually anyone from every age both sexes, every walk of life even to the rich sometimes, to the gay, the physically and mentally handicapped. How would you like to get old for example and not be wanted wherever you went? How would you like to be a

aturn

female that does not receive equal pay for the same work that men do? How would you like to be a LBTQ member (one of the little ones) that are not seen fit for society sometimes to this day? How would you like to be deaf and be false diagnosed as a schizophrenic and be treated like you are an out and out crazy person? How would you like to stutter but can get no one to give you social cover for your inability to be perfectly articulate? How would you like to have social anxiety and experience rejection just because no one would be your friend? How would you like to be black living in a self-interested white America? How would you like to be a pop and gum writer with rock music instead of with rap or hard rock and practically get show to the door just because your Beatles style is just no popular like is used to be? How would you like to be affluent and don't fit in to go play pool over on the other side of town when you were a perfectly decent person? What if you were a democrat that was turned away from where you went when for no good reason? What if you were a Republican and too were hated and discriminated against for no good no good reason too? And yes everyone's politics are different somewhat anyways.

aturn

No doubt there is a difference between adult entertainment and that which is for children. This is something that is not considered unfair discrimination though but something that just has to exist for the safety and overall good of us all!

Love of course transcends all of the differences that you can think of between people including different ages, sex, politics, or social statis, or even what taste in music that may be unique. Love says that he or she is not one of those but says this is my brother or sister or good friend and I am going to be that good friend?

So now where does delusion of all things fit into this discussion? Well now without love in our hearts for others it sometimes is replaced by hate! When there is no reason to hate others but every good reason to love others. Hate and un-necessary divisiveness between people cause one to see others in a false way that is lie about them. What's wrong with love! I for one believe that is the answer! God Bless you!

Example 65 Blind Faith

It has been a travesty throughout history that the masses have accepted being led around by the nose by political or religious leaders either one that somewhat misled the public and took them on a dark course of action. Adolf Hitler in his youth was thought to be a great comedian to some, but then he turned around and committed the most thinkable of atrocities to the Jews that has ever gone on in mankind. He told us that the Jews were an evil force..! How ridiculous! Certain religious leaders –those in fanatical fundamentalism that have gotten people to unite in a faith that relies exclusively on faith healing, while ignoring the medical truth about someone's state of health and how it should be helped and maintained and done hurt to those who believed such a thing and would not get medical help when they needed it. They are distorting a just weight to the Bible when it wants to tell us that righteousness and the Love of God inside in all that we do makes every good and positive thing happen that you can think of-literal miracle you might say that were thought to be impossible in fact! Causes that tell us to disrespect the rights of others we should not heed! Any time we get caught up a distorted idiotic movement that say others right don't count then don't go for it! No doubt we have problems of crime and

aturn

poverty, but we need a realistic approach to what we do to remedy this. My oldest and wisest brother, Ralph, once told me that change does not always happen overnight, but it is day by incremental process instead of a rash fanatical solution that does not help remedy anything but destroys the lives of the innocent in many cases. Whereas I can sometimes feel emotionally laden about an issue I do search my soul and ask am I being unfair to certain individuals in the process. When we get mad about something that it is a political issue we can tend to right off a continued commitment to the rights of all to tell yourself that you are going to "get them" that spoiled you when your mind is hyperbolating and distorting the facts to race ahead with disaster! Blind faith and blind obedience instead of sensible rational judgment that is fair to all we need not heed!

Delusion is when we believe a lie about others that distorts our understanding of reality. Let's know to be rational and civil in how we approach problems! Don't be misled by those right or left either one that will not examine all of the facts intelligently and forge ahead with an emotionally laden pathway that does not include the full truth nor is just to all!

aturn

Example 66 The Arrogance Of Wealth

 Do you know that there are people that happen to be rich that are also haughty like almost they are better than us too. That s right they show signs of being haughty like only them and their wealth counts for statis and appreciation. Fortunately these wonderful soles- many of them go thru crisis just like we all do and learn that we all count in the process. Like just because we were so high and mighty a second ago this is ultimately in the hands of God and we must learn humility and love for all. This is where the Billy Joel song comes into play for me that is called it's All about soul! Now God loves everybody including those in business that have the responsibility of money too and what they have to learn like us all is that in this world God loves us all like we should be loved. Sometimes economic or other setbacks can get one to realize that they are not God -the elite sometimes realize that they should love us all and be grateful for life. When we get enough suffering in this world we come to our senses! In the word of the Billy Joel song it goes, "It's all about soul, it's all about joy that comes out of heartache, its all about soul, it's all about soul. Oh God when we are

aturn

brought to our knees by the turbulence in life may we decide to love others more.

It is a delusion to think that just because we have more money than others that we are better than someone else. "Search me of God and know my heart today. See if there be any wicked way in me try me oh savior.. to thine I give all the Glory!" Love is even for the poor side of town and working people too! Let's learn to love one another even as Christ loved us! Love is better than just great riches! "I once was lost but now I'm found, was blind but now I see!" "Love lifted me, love lifted me when nothing else could help love lifted me!" Love is the answer to all of our problems! God Bless you!

Example 67   The Conspiracy?

It was a cold day in Montana the first day of my life where I was literally plagued by a weird experience! I was off of work on this cold February day on a Saturday when I was just twenty two yrs. old. I was driving down the road to the home supply store to buy a new shovel, as the one that I had was in terrible shape, I noticed a guy shoveling

aturn

his sidewalk in front of his house as I drove by. He had what looked like a brand new snow shovel in his hand that to me reminded me that I was about to go get a new shovel myself. It almost felt that he was even trying to send me a message that I was on the right trail to be picking up a new shovel. I never seen this guy in my life before, so it was really absurd to think that he was right now going out of his way to send me a message personally of any kind with what he was doing right now, but somehow it felt like his presence was rigged in the environment.

   As I walked into the supply store to purchase a new shovel as I entered the store I looked over at the wall where the shovels for sale were usually located, but right now there were no shovels in my sight hanging along the wall for sale there. Instead there was a guy standing in front of the wall looking right at me smiling as I began to search the wall for shovels. Like just maybe he wanted to rub it in that they were out of a new shovel for sale that you needed.   Even if he were a salesman or clerk that worked there just doing his job it made you feel like anyways that he had gone out of his way to send you a message of gloating that the new shovels were all sold out!! You didn't believe this thought but you this at least went thru your mind.

aturn

Anyways after looking around for a couple of minutes you discovered at a new location along the wall a variety of new shovels for sale. You pick out one that you think is made strong enough not to break and at the time have a razor sharp edge on the shovel to get the snow up good with. When you got up to the checkout lane there was guy ahead of you with a new shovel in his hand too. It looked a little bit sturdier than the one that you are about to purchase. Maybe he is trying to say to you to go back and get a better one yet. You have faith though in the one you already picked up to buy and you continue to check out with it.

Along the way driving home you notice a guy out shoveling his walk with a new shovel. The shovel that he is using looks like the one that the guy ahead of you in the checkout lane at the supply store bought to use.

When you get home you try out your new shovel and it breaks on you. You are of course upset and you remember the smile on the face of the guy that was checking out ahead of you at the supply store with a better shovel. You are of course upset and think that the smile on the face of the guy at the checkout lane ahead of you knew you were headed for disaster with the shovel you were about to purchase. You

aturn

wish that he had been nice enough to say something to you about the dubious quality of the shovel that you were about to purchase.

Now it is delusional to think that others were conveniently planted in the environment to probably trying to tease your head about what shovel you were about to buy when this is just not the case. It may be true that the guy in front of you in the checkout lane really thought that it was funny to him when he smiled to say that you have picked the wrong shovel, but now to think that there has been some kind of grand conspiracy on the part of several different people on this day to make fun of you about what shovel you would pick up and break- this is not to be believed. What is reality of course to you is that you have had a bad day. The end!

Example 68 Where's My Car Keys?

One day I was in a hurry to leave the house to drive somewhere in my car. For some reason I could not find my car keys that morning. I know that I had taken them out of my pocket to clean my finger nails and clip them with the nail clipper that was on the key chain with my keys. After that I could just not remember just where I left my keys. I

aturn

knew it had to be either in the kitchen or the living room thought that I left them as that was the only two places that I was since the time I cut my finger nails in the kitchen into the trash bag that was filling up quickly.

    Anyways, a few minutes later when I wanted to leave the house to go somewhere in the car I simply could not find my keys anywhere throughout the kitchen and living room both. I know that it is not plausible that someone could have stolen them even though I was watching TV in the living room after I cut my nails and someone in actuality could have come thru the front door which was open, but not the screen door. They would really have to have been quick because I only watched TV for about ten minutes after I clipped my nails in the kitchen before I then decided that I wanted to use the car to go shopping. In all honestly it was just absurd to think that someone in that short of time would have hurried from outside of your house into the kitchen, grabbed the keys from off the table in there and left. But nonetheless after searching for the keys with no success I stood in the living room and pointed my finger into the air and said, "Now, whomever thinks that they can steal my keys from me is going to be sorry in a minute." Just then while clenching my fist tight with the

aturn

other hand I realized that I had been holding my car keys in this same hand the whole time that I was looking for them and didn't realize it! My faith in my fellowman was restored and the quick scare and delusion that I just went thru was abruptly over. It was not to be believed in the first place that anybody possibly could have and would have stolen my car keys, but nonetheless I was just about believing it really could have happened and was literally having a panic attack over this whole incident. So much for sudden fear that is basically irrational...! Let's learn not to be irrational over ludicrous absurd fears and stay calm and patient.

Example 69 Puns And Double Talk!

Poor Jim Boomer was plagued all of the time by hearing puns or then double-meanings to what he hears from others. Just on one particular day he experienced better than ten double-meanings to what he heard in the form of a pun. Let me fill you in.

Early that Friday morning Jim was thinking about how the corn outside was getting tall while at the same time he had the morning news on TV on. A newsman came on and said to the other newsmen

aturn

sitting beside him my "big ears" last night picked up a little bit of good gossip! This then makes a simple pun for Jim-no confusion about it.

- While driving to work on this same morning you are listening to the rock station while you happen to be thinking about a female you love very much. The radio disc jockey says of a glamorous Hollywood female that with her kind of money she is literally buying the stairway to heaven. You think about the female that you love so very much is just a little bit richer than you and is right now getting into the M column pretty strong. Instead of feeling hopeful right ow that she will come back to you. (What a thought with no faith that your girl will every come back to you based on just a fleeting thought that could be false because of the influence of what you just heard said on the radio.) When you arrive at work on this morning you realize that on this late spring day that the window of the plant are crocked open at the bottom to let the fresh air in. As you step out of the car A friend yells over to you from over on the other side of the parking lot, "How you doin'?" You yell back to him, "well now great now that I get to go to work…" He ran up to you and said I got a joke with a pun to it, "there was this female that started to have a photographic memory, but never developed it. Get that one Jim?" Jim said back, "yea I get it!" You thought this joke is harmless!

aturn

When Jim got into the factory cafeteria he over-heard two people talking about a chicken farmer. The one guy said to the other guy, "this same chicken farmer's favorite car is a coupe." To which they both laughed at together. Well here was another experience that you had on this day that concerned a pun that was harmless to anyone.

Just a few minutes later in route to the time clock to punch in Jim heard two guys walking the other way down the aisle saying one to the other, "that guy is sure a pain in the ass!" You at least think that he might have been referring to you but you are not positive about this. You see Jim has just been working in this place for less than a year and does not know everybody or even how to do everything around here like some that work here can and even has a slight inferiority complex if teased by others. Well this double talk that he overheard hurt him inside and even more than that made him mad. He was at least trying and the only reason that he could not do any better in performance on the job than he presently does was his lack of experience that he had as far as he was concerned.

Anyways lunch-time finally arrived for Jim and he hurried to the cafeteria to get his sandwich out of the refrigerator along with a pop that he brought also and eat and drink to contentment. Well now when Jim walked into the cafeteria he had just been thinking about a female that he loved and dated but no longer was seeing. He overheard one young man say to another young man while smiling, "she is going out with me tonight and I know that she is good…..!" This makes Jim freak inside because he really think that he just might be talking about the same female that he dated a short time ago and still loved. Ew this double meaning to what someone just said that you think might have been directed towards you personally as you were hurt so bad by this female …! Now to have someone to rub it in like this is really hurtful.

The rest of the day at work you yet at work experienced just one more double-meaning to what one said that also hurt you as you were just about to leave work for the day. You are lined up at the time clock about to punch out when you overhear two people talking behind you in the line. One of them said to the other one, that guy up there ahead of us is a real jackass. You did not know for sure that they were talking about you, but you think so. All in all one, two, three time on this day you experienced what was derogatory double-talk that was intended as a comment about you.

Poor Jim suffers from a persecution complex where his mind exaggerates the effect of the true meaning of others bull-shit talk sometimes. Perhaps they are just kidding with him and he is taking what they say more seriously than they really mean it?! Like maybe he just don't know these other people well enough to even make out how they kid with others just for the fun of it. Jim does not quit where he works just because he feels a little rejection and four years later he is a supervisor and eight yrs. later runs the whole plant for good money! Turn your circumstances around with a big attitude to keep on truckin' during adversity and the sun will always come back again if you're good! God Bless You!

Example 70 I'm The Stage Act!

I was twenty-two yrs. old that when I looked around it looked like all eyes were upon me. Like I was being watched by literally everyone even though I was sure that this was not the case at all. Anyways this thrust me to a new feeling all the time of being like I was the center of attention to the whole world, and I was now too like the leading actor on a stage in everyday life in all that I did. All of the other people immediately in front of me or behind my back were merely the supporting actors to my lead role. At least sometimes what others did right in front of me in the same environment for instance struck me like a cue to me to perform better in whatever I was doing. For example when I needed to get back to jogging before or after work, some of my co-workers appeared to me to be dropping me hints that I need to lose weight somehow soon. When I walked past the maintenance crib there was a guy that worked in there that was already fat but now when I walked by him in the main aisle he would stick out his stomach further in mock imitation of what the fat on me looked like. Another guy every time he seen you from anywhere in the plant would pretend to be jogging right in front of me to give me the idea to get running soon. Then yet another guy yelled all the way across the room " lard bucket" in my direction to give me the idea that I need to lose some weight faster.

Now it turns out that I resumed jogging again like my own intuition had been telling me too and I lost fifty pounds. I often think of the song mind games by John Lennon where he talks about fostering a spirit of peace on earth by apparently just giving each other right vibrations and gumption to get there with what we should be. This is a positive interpretation of the "mind games" that people could play in everyday life, but that can happen too just as easily as the altogether seriously unwelcoming and unfriendly vibrations that others could give us, if we ourselves become more positive in how we treat others. May the day come when people sing like King Harvest endorsed,

aturn

"everybody here is out of sight, they don't bark and they don't bite, everybody was dancing in the moonlight! May we experience a day too like John Fogerty talked about in Lookin Out My Backdoor where even all the animals come out and are our friend!

Example 71 Is A Positive Imagination Always Good?

I'm of the persuasion that by and large a positive imagination related to all of our dreams coming true is good and not bad! That's right just because you imagine yourself a greater success, and/or a more fulfilled person can motivate us to get there with our ambition in many cases, and does not necessarily mean that we just live in a fantasy world that is unrealistic. Of course at least sometimes we can wish for something to happen and just because we wish for it we believe that it will necessarily come to its fruition when this is not to be believed. Consider a guy that is madly in love with a female where she has made it clear that the relationship between him and her is over. He however cannot accept that this is the case, so finally she has to file a restraining order on him to get him to finally leave her alone for good. Consider too another scenario where a young man wants to make the big time with his rock music. He is not too bad, but he just lacks exciting enough original material of his own to make this possible even though he has already been writing many songs for years. He has been told already by the people that run the radio stations and stage itself that he is just not good enough for "The Big Time." He continues on though and spends a vast amount of his savings still to try and make this happen when there is no realistic reason to believe that it will. He literally lives in a fantasy of being the star instead of just be happy and continue on with his interest of singing with a realistic attitude that accepts that competition is real and in this case better than he can come up with. Yet a third scenario of where someone is living in a fantasy of possibility that is unrealistic is a guy that wants to get rich, but has no realistic means to do this. He spends more money than he can realistically in everyday life and is just plain digging himself in debt further and further. He needs of course to accept reality and live within his means instead of wistful thinking to change the fact that he is poor and probably always will be. "Yes" it is possible to go overboard with unrealistic expectations for ourselves in many cases. This would not stop me however from telling the next generation to keep dreaming wishing and hoping for a better and more fulfilled life, but don't stay in

aturn

a unrealistic fantasy world that is a lie sometimes about what is realistically possible in this regard!

Example 72 How Do We Construe Good And Evil?

Like as is the case with all other words and concepts it is after all how we define this word or concept that makes it clear what it is we are actually talking about. According to Merriam Webster dictionary this word good means conforming to the moral order of the universe. According to Merriam Webster dictionary the word evil means morally reprehensible, sinful, and wicked. Well now you can gather from how we define these two words that good or goodness is that which helps sustain life, but evil is that which destroys it. No doubt there are things that we can do that can be help to each other survive and excel for the betterment of us all, while there are yet other things that we can do that hurt each other un-necessarily.

One thing to keep in mind should be not to be deceived by appearances, but only judging others in a fully objective manner as it pertains to anything. Many, many people-especially church goers seem to think that a pious appearance or even a place- namely the church is good while those who mix out there in the real world that like a cold beer get condemned by them even when they can drink in moderation only. Is good or evil I had a beer in itself or is safety the issue here? So that one drinks in moderation to the point that they are safe may mean no harm to anyone.

To me in one big sense a work ethic and results from that, that are positive constitute good as this can in many cases make progress for all of us. It is sloth and unwarranted gossip that we should detest!

The delusion can be then that we may really think that good is just a pious appearance instead of a work –ethic with proven results. Let's get to work to build a good world for us all! Amen!

Example 73 Double Meanings To What One Sees Or Thinks About!

There was a man named Bob Zabo that was going thru a phase where he had problems with his nerves. Every time he looked around in the same environment he would notice something that was additional to what you could just literally see in itself. When he saw a guy sweeping with a broom, instead of just seeing it at that level, what he

aturn

experienced was a second meaning coming alive to it where Bob then believed this literal act of sweeping the floor right in front of him was indeed a personal hint and innuendo that he was not going anywhere- like unto greater job opportunity or greater wealth either one. And when Bob noticed that the supervisor always turned away from him when he noticed him, he experienced this on another level to imply to him that even as he had thoughts of becoming a supervisor and was going to ask this same guy about opportunity in this regard he took it what the supervisor was literally doing right in front of him was to make a bigger point to him personally that he was not wanted in supervision. And then when Bob saw a guy swinging his arms like a monkey as he walked that he was really doing a mock imitation of how he himself walked just to hurt his pride. And when Bob would think about the upcoming presidential election he would imagine that the presidential candidate that he supported was not holding a rally in Bob's hometown just because he did not care about Bob in any special way even after Bob put up campaign signs in his yard to support him. And when Bob thought about why his sister always yelled at him on the phone to vote democrat it was really because she was partisan to the point that she was unfair as opposed to she could in good conscience support their crummy agenda at the level of the presidency. In Bob's mind his sister was not a patriotic person anymore because she abandoned the right security position on illegal immigration. Her stand was too weak where we could soon be overrun by another country....! He thought now not even the red, white and blue, flag that Betsy Ross made will be preserved, but oligarchy in its place on the way soon if we do not protect our borders from illegal immigration.

Now none of Bob's thoughts were illogical altogether, but he seemed to be reading in more real meaning to what others may have been trying to imply to him which in reality was nothing at all. This fuller way of thinking like Bob is now experiencing does not necessarily mean that Bod is going crazy but just seeing more potential meaning to the behavior of others than he once did where it is possible even to guess right a special meaning that someone may have been conveying to him- like real symbolic communication in the form of a message. Most of the time in fact when Bob noticed a second meaning coming alive to what others did right in front of him or imagined it behind his back a special meaning being deliberately sent to him in the form of a message using symbolic communication it is just a runaway imagination on his part. Bob is really now analyzing behavior on a higher order than he once did and is almost jumping to false conclusion about the meaning of others behavior. When and if he assumes that others were trying to send him a message when better evidence suggest otherwise than he sometimes could be said to be delusional. Learning not to be in too much of a hurry to jump to a conclusion about the meaning of others behavior becomes something to learn for Bob.

Example 74 Is Old Fashioned Love Just a Delusion?

All the time I hear lately from others that this world is going to perish if there is not enough old fashioned love in this world! I myself agree with that wholeheartedly, but yet others would say that love does not really exist, but obligation instead. If that's true that would mean that we really do all of the positive things that we do for others just because it is expedient or in some way or otherwise to our own advantage. I for one resent this kind of reasoning that leaves out that real love does in fact exist; but claims that we are delusional if we are to say we have love in our hearts for others when they really did what they did for their own selfish benefit. Huh!

Did mother Teresa who spent her life in India as a missionary do so for greed? And when people volunteered to help with the corona virus were they indeed getting a monetary kick back for that or are they indeed really a hero? And when the police and fire department exceed what they must do to keep us alive shouldn't that be equated with bravery beyond obligation? And when that twelve year old young man that was chubby with black hair did not listen to the gang but to his own heart to shovel the old poor lady's walk across the street for free while they were laughing-would you say that he was obligated to do so? And when you are broke and your good friend Bernie spends half a day helping you to keep your car on the road when he didn't have to wasn't that a selfless deed?! And when the shopkeeper saved every extra cent he had to help the poor was this just for esteem? And when your mom or dad remain your good friend after eighteen did they really have to do this or is it because deep down inside they love you with all their heart or is it because they don't love you?!

Finally brothers and sisters this world really does need more love in it and this need not be seen as hypocrisy, demogogery or even a delusion of some kind! Now let's love each other and end pain and suffering here on earth! It is possible of course to really care for others expecting nothing in return but the joy love puts in your heart for being a friend to others! God Bless You! A loveless world is really the delusional one!

Example 75 Is Romantic Love A Delusion?!

One time one of my very favorite professors at IUSB was in a bad mood when he started his lecture. He grinned at all of us and said, I know love don't really exist because I have lived too long to believe that. Well now I didn't smile or see one on the face of any other students when he said this nor laughter from any of us, but I smile all the time by now when I remember what he said that day while opening his lecture. Tom was literally the best of guys even if he was a right winger and I barely am still a democrat that reserves the right to vote for anyone I want to vote for on election- day. He was I'm sure talking about romantic love when he said it cause he looked like just maybe him and his honey hadn't been getting along. I'd rather laugh with this professor than at him!

Anyways, a whole lot of people are going to tell me also that with their experiences in life that romantic love is illusive, slippery, and even a delusion itself. I don't like to talk about my own private experience with romance, but I am going to tell you that even though two different females broke my heart when I was a kid and I have no one special to this day that I think that romantic love indeed exists. Even though we couldn't make things work out to stay together I'm sure that I love both of them to this day just as much as I did way back when I first met them. I care about both of them very much to this day and that is what it really means to love someone is to care for them! I think of the second female that I loved very much and still have hope that someday she will accompany me all the way to the Justice of the Peace or the alter at the Penticostal church! I like the words of the song by Bob Seger that says, "Someday lady you'll accompany me. Someday lady you'll accompany me, it's written in the stars you see, but someday lady you'' accompany me."

Anyways whether romantic love reflects a picture back that we believe is real is up to the individual to decide and purely a matter of opinion! If romance now makes you feel like the whole thing was just a mirage or whatever where you were tricked into believing that which was transient and potentially changing then you can doubt it is real if you want to unto calling it a delusion by some people's estimation. But I say unto both of those two females from then that "I'm going to keep on loving you because it the only thing I want to do!" God bless my sweethearts to this day. Let's keep love alive! It is real to me!

Example 76 Is Agape Love Really Delusion?

Agape love may be defined as selfless, sacrificial, unconditional, and rational love, and is the highest form of love. This could be thought to be synonym's with old fashioned love in many situations, but agape love of course gives a stronger emphasis on how just for one this kind of love is unconditional love. The love of a parent for their children is a perfect example of agape love most of the time. Parents don't love their children one day and the next don't love them just because their kid may have made a mistake or does not excel yet in anything special that the parent would be proud of. Their love for their children is unwavering, so that they will always love their children.

Now just like old fashioned love and romantic love, Agape love is sometimes doubted and low and behold obligation itself or personal advantage is the real reason why let's say parents love their children the way they do. This kind of reasoning though is admonished though as untrue and offensive to those who have shown great care towards others every day that is unwavering. People that are a "Big player" in life simply do not always become this way just because they were pushed to, and/or have something to gain from this, but they simply stand out, head and shoulders above others in terms of how much they show they care every day for others! Agape love or a "big love' that should in actuality then be thought to be a guiding force inside us that we have incorporated somewhere along the journey in life. A kind word spoken to others or a selfless thoughtful deed for others….. A soldier or a police officer laying down their life for all of us…a writer that takes the time to introspect, analyze, and deliver on something worth-while that we all should know… The lady who bakes the cakes for the poor kids and gets nothing in return back but the gratification of having done a nice deed for others….!

In Hebrews chapter 6 St. Paul challenges us to love others even as God loved Israel or then of course with infinite love for us all. My sentiment is that we are not here just to enjoy and fulfill our life as much as possible, but that we should give something back with our efforts that show we care for others by making progress here on earth that is of course for all of us! Yes I myself am sure anyways that a big love for others can be possible instead mediocrity, which is not hypocrisy but glorious in its effect!

Now for those who still would still doubt that old fashioned is real I would suggest sometimes that perhaps they are the ones that are delusional. "Tell the devil he can freeze up!"

Example 77 A Photographic Memory!!!

When I was at the ripe old age of 22yrs. old I achieved what at least is close to a photographic memory in terms of what went on around me in the immediate environment from the time I got out of bed till the time I went back to bed. What this new way of experiencing reality did was wake up my mind to all kinds of things going on around me, especially in the traffic out in the road that I did not used to notice at all. Let me explain this giving you examples of what was new and different than I once noticed out in the road. My now keener memory began to pick up on all kinds of things out there that I just did not notice before. For example I noticed that on any given day that there might be always the same number of motor vehicles that were driving out ahead of me numerous times on that day and not just once. I thought am I to believe that this is the undercover police driving out ahead of me for my protection? I also noticed that on any given day there might be an overwhelming amount of cars out in the road that were the same color. I thought too with this, could this be the undercover police that were keeping an eye out for me for my safety or a whole lot of people with what sometimes appeared to be a maneuver of some sort right in front of me? After thinking it over I reasoned that it indeed was probably the undercover police that were doing this probably for my safety or the safety of all of the people out in the road! Like just maybe the "heat" is on out there in a way that not everyone might even notice!

aturn

I was indeed sure and still am about what I just noticed out in the street to be real and not imagined, but a lot of other questions still remained in my mind related to who it was that did this and what was there motive behind it.

Next, I do know that it helps to put into perspective whatever you may have just experienced in the immediate environment let's right in front of you. One should ask one's self what is the: who, what, where, why, and how related to what you may have just seen. Who is it that perpetrated whatever that you many have noticed right in front of you in the same environment? Second, what exactly could they have been said to do or be doing? Third, where did this occur we should know also to acquire a pertinent detail about this? Fourth we should ask ourselves why or what is the motive behind what this person did? Fifth and last how did they go about doing this? If we just answer these five particular questions this will put into proper perspective a much fuller more meaningful understanding of what actually happened and why it may have happened! We might then know who it was who did or is possibly behind who did what you experienced that is in question.

Example 78 Zambi

aturn

Now let me tell you something right here and now that it is not nice to belittle people with mental problems to the point that we call someone a "Zambi." Instead of course we should be calling them by their first name and say" how you doin" to them!

A psychotic no doubt sometimes resembles the ficticious characteristics of a zambi in like that a zambi walks around dumbfounded in a world of their own. I have no doubt that when someone came up with the concept of a zambi they were really hinting at those who are sometimes in a world of their own with schizophrenia and other psychotic disorders.

Somewhere along the way in life this person usually felt rejected and/or betrayed by others so that they turned inward constructing a reality of their own that gave an explanation of others behavior that without full honesty about things they don't want to accept-like maybe they have an inferiority complex deep down inside that they need to grow out of instead of blame others or retreat into a world of their own.

If we are to help get this person to come out of their withdrawal and back into their right mind, we must show them that we love them and that we think that they have self-worth and count too! Is that any too big a deal to be a friend to others once in a while to rescue your friend from fear, doubt, and lack of self-confidence instead of give up on them! Love the sick and the lost! Did not someone love us including the Good Shephard himself?! Let's get people to come back into their right mind and be a winner and an overcomer and your now new friend now shining bright! I know it can be done! So love others and make them feel like they count!

Example 79 Concerned About Crime Or A Bigot?

Now these are not just ordinary peace loving times in America! First, the police cannot even keep their eye on what all of the young people in the next generation are really up to in their free time. There is a lot of crime of drug peddling just for one and lot of gangs that the police can' always just break up. Young people usually in crime are on the loose sometime in their teens in many cases driving around without a carrier's permit with a loaded pistol or even a semi-automatic to potentially inflict great harm on other people. There is a shooting almost every day in most major cities right now. I mean there is crime and violence that is real and dangerous to us all!

Now the police have the unenviable job of keeping the peace, and safety for us all in an era where there is runaway crime and a lot of backlash from the public in how they do their job. They are put in harm's way every minute on the job by paying attention to those that are in crime that in many cases are armed and dangerous. I have mixed feelings about the influence about the influence of the Black Lives Matter Movement. On the one hand everyone with a heart or conscience wishes that police don't go overboard with what they do when they have to apprehend a suspect using no more force than they really have to, to bring in their man! But tell me if you try to resist arrest by punching the police let's say do you think that they are going to then hand you a lolly pop or necessary force that it takes to bring in a suspect?! And now if someone appears to be reaching for a weapon that could kill you do you suppose the police just might open fire on you in return instead of possibly get shot. There are police that are a good man that get shot every day by a no good rascal in crime! How do you like that?! And what if the police did not get their man that is potentially armed and dangerous, but he or she then gets away from them them couldn't that be dangerous to us all?! Heaven help us all if we do not let the police do what it takes to bring in their man! Without the force of the coercion of the state we have anarchy instantly! And does somebody that is bad want to reap a positive reward for evil and try to con the system to do their will! Heaven help us all! Do people that know nothing about law enforcement now trying to run the police?! Ew'man that is going too far.......!

aturn

Let me right now say a prayer of safety for our fine police that risk their lives every day to keep us alive! Oh God protect our police that risk their lives for all of us every day! May God bless our police!

Now if you are to take the position to support your local police like I do tthat then make you a bigot or concerned citizen?! Love and support our police!

To me that is delusional to confuse a concern for the safety of us all by misconstruing the meaning of what they do that is overwhelmingly for the good of all of us. Someone is full of a lot of simple-minded wheweee and its not me! They can't see past the end of their nose and dos not register the consequence of trying to dismantle our police department. Do you think that would really do the general public any good that should be good? Understanding that includes even potential reform from time to time for police strategies in how to carry out their job better when it is in order, but those that know nothing about law enforcement trying to run the police department-NO!

Example 80 It's Always Been A Matter Of Trust

As it pertains to how we run the police departments throughout United States of America it is first good to keep the morale high among

aturn

the uniformed police that are out their everyday somewhere in the real world keeping us all of us safe!

This lecture for all of us to hear talks about what I believe is the right attitude for all of those in law enforcement to adhere to. There are five personality characteristics that someone that wants to be in law enforcement should know about. They are first confidence, second, working together with other fraternal brothers and sister effectively or then comrade-reship. Third, one needs to exhibit the quality and characteristic of integrity or then someone of moral principle, Fourth, one must be loyal to the cause of upright law enforcement to be accepted in the long run. Fifth and final one must be overall altogether trustworthy to wear the badge of an American police officer!

First, we need to have much confidence on the job as a police officer. We need confidence in that we know that we are going to get our man with an arrest instead of he or she is still at large and we did not do our job effectively enough! And then we need confidence also that when we run into bad guys out there that we are really going to live and the other innocent people too in the same vicinity, and then it takes confidence too, to believe that day after day for perhaps thirty one can always achieve the positive results that one should when put under cricumstance.

Second, we need team work or then comradriship while working on the job. It really takes dedicated police willing to work together to achieve maximum results. Anything less than that could be disastrous for everyone- not only the police but the public at large with them. Team work is a "definite" for consistently acceptable results!

Third we need integrity in the police department – "strict adherence to moral and ethical principles; soundness of moral character; honesty, the state of being whole entire or unconditional." (Dictionary. Com) We definitely need men and women of upright character that really do exhibit the qualities of honesty, moral and ethical character to possess and maintain a group of trustworthy individuals best suited for the job! A police department is no better than the men and women that work for it!

Fourth, we need loyalty among those that work in the police department meaning that they are "faithful to commitments or obligations" (Dictionary.com) in the interest of not letting each other down when we may of course be desperately needed to tackle the job. Being short-handed on the police department because someone did not show up for work really prevents maximum results in law enforcement from going on! It could even be disastrous in more than one way for

aturn

the police to be short just one man or woman on the job that can be a vital player for genuine and complete success.

Fifth, we need trustworthiness by the police to be true to their duties. To be trustworthy of course means to be dependable or reliable. We need first class work out of our police all the time! It is this kind of attitude and record in a police department that makes for maximum results.

So now how does delusion of all things come along on the topic of loyalty and commitment to the police department? Well if you were or still are someone that thinks a truly committed police department with high ideals doesn't matter or is just a lot of nonsense, you are believing a lie even after you have just been very briefly filled in on the importance of true commitment to one's job on the police department! Believe it or not this could be considered a delusion on your part. Know the truth that it indeed does take commitment from those who are in the police to make the whole institution run like it should! Anything else is a lie or deceived mind!

Example 81 "Old Glory!"

aturn

Today some people are challenging the idea that we really have such a thing as freedom saying that it just an abstract concept with no real substantial meaning to it. This I am going to refute back right here and now acknowledging that freedom is no doubt an abstract concept, but it indeed exists with real meaning to it. The phrase …"thy liberty in law.." by Kathreen Lee Bates in the second verse of America The Beautiful is referring of course to the bill of Rights in the constitution, including freedom of speech, press, the right to peaceable assembly, thee right to vote, freedom of religion, and the right to bear arms etc. These so called rights in the bill of rights mandates what turns into concrete and real freedom for us in everyday life that we all may take advantage of.

As the old saying goes with freedom comes responsibility! These freedoms declared in the bill of right are not unconditional sometimes but still do exist for us! And you can't say that we are not doing quite a bit to help everybody in this country at the same time.

As it pertains to delusion because the concepts of freedom and right are complex they still reflect real freedom for us! It is really those who think that freedom is just an abstract concept with no meaning that are either lying or have actually deceived themselves into believing this which would then make it delusional. Let's not be delusional, but forge

aturn

ahead taking advantage of the many rights that we do have! God bless you!

Example 82 A Whole Circle Of Perspectives May Be Relevant!

Neither Ellen Degeneres nor Russ Limbaugh-two people diametrically opposed in politics, capture my conscience for what I truly believe in. I believe in fact it takes a whole circle of perspectives if we are going to make the best progress possible in our society. I think truth is neither all to the right or all left, but the problem that is glaringly real and presently upon us dictates what kind of remedy would be best in many cases!

To be dogmatic insist that the right or left either one is always right is to err or even be come delusional in some cases! Partisan politics is atrocious! And isn't it nice too that we can ignore the opinion of the "special people" to be more honest with ourselves about what we believe! Believing and trusting in partisan politics or the "special people" either one sometimes can be delusion instead of truth as the final product! Let's not be delusional!

aturn

Example 83 Mood Swings!

According to The Mayo Clinic: **Overview**

Bipolar disorder, formerly called manic depression, is a mental health condition that causes extreme mood swings that include emotional highs (mania or hypomania) and lows (depression).

When you become depressed, you may feel sad or hopeless and lose interest or pleasure in most activities. When your mood shifts to mania or hypomania (less extreme than mania), you may feel euphoric, full of energy or unusually irritable. These mood swings can affect sleep, energy, activity, judgment, behavior and the ability to think clearly.

Episodes of mood swings may occur rarely or multiple times a year. While most people will experience some emotional symptoms between episodes, some may not experience any.

Although bipolar disorder is a lifelong condition, you can manage your mood swings and other symptoms by following a treatment plan. In most cases, bipolar disorder is treated with medications and psychological counseling (psychotherapy).

Right here and now though I contend that bipolar is a façade of a sort that if it really does exist at all can be overcome in time. What I want to stress about this so-called dreaded disorder is that I

am sure in my own mind that there is no real innate abnormality that causes mood swings at all, but that it is really a situationally caused problem that with better reasoning about your own self and the willingness to acquire patience manic depressive behavior or what they call bipolar by now will really go away.

Let's take the example of someone that happens to be writing a good book that will have to be 500 pages long in order to fulfill the task it's mean't to do. On one day this same person may have tremendous success in forging ahead with what they are writing. Let's say that they accomplished getting ten solid pages done in just two days after really working hard on their project. The first emotion that follows is one of elation and joy that they could have achieved getting what happened to be a very difficult part of the book. But then when he woke up the very next morning he is that I did, but at the moment it seems futile thee whole project because he has yet about another 190 pages to go before he is done writing just the rough draft of it. So then it was just his situation that the book he was writing was going to take very long time to write was the real reason for the mood swings that he had and not some kind of innate abnormality, but instead his own immaturity and lack of patience that caused him not to stay level headed with what he was doing. He could learn patience and staying level headed just as soon as he, on the conscious level of his mind realized and accepted that the book he were writing is going to take a little time to write so don't get so up-tight about it.

Let's take yet another example of where someone might be said to be someone that has mood swings. There was this guy that was terribly talented and creative also in like he sang and wrote funny short stories, but nothing had ever become of it like that he was offered to sing for money even though he hoped it would eventually happen still. And then too he wrote some real fun short stories about being a friend to others, but they never sold but a few copies each. So on the one hand when he got a hot hand with his music or singing either one he could feel first very high about it, but when he would come around to realizing there was no future for money in what he did it would bring him to despair. Now if he had just admitted to himself that it was not likely that his music or sing either one were going anywhere, and accepted reality accordingly then his mood swings would subside. He had no inherent innate abnormality in his mind, just a lack of understanding one's own self better that can be accomplished if we are becoming more awake an realizing that our disorder is situationally caused and not by some unknown force. .

aturn

Now that is indeed my rebuttle to the, by now conventional knowledge that bipolar as it is now called for mood swings is not a permanent disorder. In reality it just takes knowing yourself better related to your own illness plus the need for more patience and full honesty with one's self that will overcome it. An enlightened mind and time itself changes our situation for the better to not experience fear and dread over simple mood swings. I recommend instead of pills in the long run for mood swings "knowing yourself better related to your situation" is the key to overcoming a disorder that can overcome entirely and not just controlled with dope. I am an optimist about the possibility of all overcoming mood swings and learn to keep a more constant frame of mind- one that knows and accepts reality well enough, instead of just being tossed around with mood swings for sure. The optimist for sure that bi-polar can be overcome is the one that is not delusional between the two.

Just between you and me if you really believe in the pursuit only of counselors and anti-psychotic drugs that admittedly can only subdue the symptoms of bi-polar, instead of a pathway to full self-enlightenment thru more effort with work and love, then you will stay delusional instead. What a fool believes he or she receives! But if you learn to know yourself better by waking up your own mind more you

aturn

can register the cause and effect of mood swings-which is situational- and then you can learn not to get shook about a mood swing but know patience, tolerance, endurance, and consistency.

Example 85 God Is A Good God

    I remember very vividly back in the sixties on Sunday morning after delivering my paper route that Brother Oral Roberts would come on our TV to preach encouragement to all believers. He would say, "expect a miracle" "something good is going to happen to you", "make your point of contact", and "God is a Good God." This of course was nice to hear no matter who you are. Well to make a long story short the saying God is a Good God always gave me a chuckle, and I didn't mean it as blasphemy.

I don't know, I guess I was glad that God was a good God instead of a bad God or evil God. That God loves us to the point that he was willing to sacrifice His own Son on the cross to save mankind instead of damn him. I think well hallelugiah God loves me and wants me to be a winner too by the way. I too am the royalty of God I thought with God inside!

aturn

Anyways when you look around and see only the suffering in life we might think that God does not love man, but when you see the influence of people with God's love inside of them- many of them are doing exploits to make this place somewhere where there is no suffering thru love inside of us! Even nature can be tamed or overcome when you have plenty of good people full of God and goodness all pulling together to make this a better world. We are more than conqueror with God's love inside us for others- to be help and not to hurt- to teach love and not hate-to care more than just for our own enjoyment even though this can come along sometimes, but bigger than just that to be committed to progress and caring for others- everyone……! The influence of God inside us definitely solves the world's problems and helps make a happier world. Think in terms of God wanting us to be a happy harmonious creation with love for one another! This is the dream, faith and hope of those who are big enough to follow after righteousness to make a better world-full of love and goodness! God is a good God and the devil is a liar!

To hate God for all the suffering in this world is to err and be delusional, but to join God with Love and Commitment to making this world a better place that is not living a lie! God Bless You!

aturn

Example 86 What Happened To The Money?

Now I know that there are ways and means to help keeping yourself from writing a bad check, but no one is perfect and to forget to write down a check while in the fast-lane can happen to just anybody! The other day my checking account was overdrawn. I was sure in my head right on the spur of the moment that someone had robbed my account, as I could in my head account for all of my checks and if all of them posted it would still not be enough spend to overdraw my account! Who could have robbed my account was what went thru my head? But then I remembered a fifty dollar debit from my checking account to fill up the gas tank this morning. This would explain the overdraft!

For just a moment I were delusional or at least made a bad assumption without knowing all the facts, thinking someone robbed my bank account when it was just not true. I jumped to a false conclusion with the utmost of subjective feeling that the theft had gone on....! By now I most of the time am not quick to rush to judgement about anything I'm not sure of, but I indeed thought just for just a moment that someone could have stolen from my bank account when the culprit was me! I tell myself every day not to be quick to jump to false conclusions about others, but know all the relevant facts before we jump to a conclusion!! Think, think, think, always!

Example 87 The Other Band

In rock music there is competition between the rivalying rock bands over who gets booked for the stage. I am a peace and love hippie that knows that competition is real sometimes, but that wishes to get along even with competitors when possible. Jesus said, "love thine enemies… " and who knows if we can all do that than just maybe we could learn to love each other too!

Anyways I had a bad experience where I at least thought that a competing band was doing low down things to compete me from competing. It turns out that even though it was real what I experienced that was a hindrance to was real and not imagined; who I attributed this too turned out to be false and it was just a series of coincidences of setbacks that made me think that the other band had done this when in reality it was all just a coincidence.

The big night came where my band was playing a big gig, but at the same time with this same band that I thought was mine enemy playing right beside me in the show. God forgive me for my misgivings and ill-founded suspicions about them and others in general for that matter! We had a great time together and we are now doing gigs together and are great friends. Love is a beautiful thing! God Bless you

aturn

Example 87 Oh Happy Day!

   I still remember the night that I repented and made a pact with God to love others at 21 yrs. old.

It was not so much the things that I had done to hurt others that bothered my conscience, but what I had not done to be help to others! Look, I was no bank robber! I told God that I want love in my heart for everyone and in everyday life be no respecter of persons instead of just play games with the crowd. I wanted respect from other people and felt willing to now do what it takes to get that respect from virtually everyone. I indeed was changed for the better after this meeting and for the rest of my life too. I now became bolder and more aggressive in my interactions with others winning new friends and more respect from others too! I had love in my heart for virtually everyone now! I was now also more eager to use my abilities to be help to all, making progress on this earth! Again, I literally became a changed person for the better! Love had lifted me from mediocrity to a Big winner!

   And now when I look back at my past before I decided that Real Love that comes from God was the answer I had misunderstandings between me and others that should not have been. I seen my experiences that I had with others showed an inability to not get along

aturn

with them sometimes. Why if I just had a little more love in my heart for others- the will to be friendly sometimes-and the willingness to be fair altogether with a more positive attitude towards others I would see others in a new light. "Holy Moses I have been deceived he or she is my brother let us live in peace!"(Elton John) I had been believing a lie that I could never have friends and success like others. I had been believing a lie that I could not be the winner and overcomer that I should be in everyday life. I altogether did not believe in myself or others either one like I should! But now with Love inside even the Love of God I became more than a conqueror helping to make progress for all of us! Whom the Son sets free is free indeed! I was now basking in a reality with dazzling sunlight of love and happiness! Instead of hate or apathy in me love would now go round and round to others. I was turning into someone that you could respect, admire, and put your trust in! Satan (the force of destruction and all evil) is a liar! We can be winners and someone that we are proud of with God's Love inside even though he does not want us to believe this! We need not live in a false reality or delusion that we are nothing and no one else is either when we all can become the Royalty of God's family right here on earth! Oh happy day happy day when Jesus un-blinded my eyes and let me see that we could love each other and have contentment and gave

aturn

me the boldness and confidence to become the person that I should be! My cup runneth over!

Example 88 Towards A Full Enlightenment

Even after I became a Christian, (even though this brought me out of a rut and gave me new peace and joy inside that would stay) I would still have an uphill climb in my life sometimes! We have much growing up to do past an initial commitment to love others with God's love inside. I told myself that I wanted all of the virtues that the Bible speaks of to be in me! That's right I wanted to grow into nobility inside or then become a noble self; not one based on birth- right but on goodness inside that comes from God. If now I really love somebody with God's love inside I will reason that if I now love others that I should do my share of the work to be help….! And if I love others I will not lie or steal from them but be honest in all ways! And if I love others I will not be mean unto inhumane treatment of them, but show love and kindness towards others! And if I love others I will be safe so that I don't hurt others! And if I really love others I will route for their happiness or success too, or then goodwill! And if I really love my wife and family I will be committed to them! And if I love my country and the freedoms that we have I should be willing to protect and stand up for continued freedom! And if I really care about my own self but others too I will value education to become a competent knower in whatever field bringing us to betterment for everybody as a result! "Do unto others as you would have them do unto you!" And when we have incorporated all these good values we will of course could be said to virtuous unto nobility. Literally all of the virtues should grow inside us if we have the attitude that we love others! If love is truly our guide goodness or then all of the virtues we will develop and live by!

It is delusion to believe that a virtuous person is just some kind of act just because we must obey the law, but we may deep down be guided by Love inside which finds a way to show we care for others in a complete and mature way! And self-development unto enlightenment is real! " surely goodness and mercy shall follow me all the days of my life.." I want all the virtues extolled in the Bible inside of me. I want respect from others plus the joy inside that it brings to really care for other and not take them for granted or rip them off. I want to be a dude that smells like Old Spice inside and not a reprehensible moron that stinks! I want caught up in heavenly places with Christ Jesus who was perfect for His age in how He treated others! Jesus said be perfect with God! Jesus said this is my commandment that ye love one another

aturn

even as I have love you also....love brings peace, joy, and happiness! I will to be a blessing to others and not a curse!

Example 89 Life Is What You Make it!

The real truth is about life that you don't get anything more out of life than you put into it. For people that do nothing but complain and remind you of loss, might I interject that no one wins that is humpty dumpty or a couch potato.

I love entertainment and even though it looks like a closed door right now I still sing, write songs, and even debut them. I am not living a delusion or illusion to say to myself that I want to commit myself to singing and being a free- lance writing. What if I just ran from the rest of the world and hid my talents under a bushel! Depart from me you wicked and abominable person that does not use their God-inspired intuition to add something for brighter day for all of us. Is it really the money end that counts like a good attitude to follow thru with what we do where we really belong to be help? "This little light of mine I"m going to let it shine" until the lost are found, the blind see, and there is a smile of love and happiness on every face. God Bless You!

aturn

Example 90 Fairness!

When it comes to business there is bound a will to sell whatever good or service that they have to offer to the point that sales of whatever good or service become number one in terms of priority and not just principle about the true value of the good of service that creeps into the scenario. Business has the special people to heed the most like the drug industry in general even when pills are killing people every day. To frequently the psychiatrists too that prescribe pills for people cater to the drug industry's incasseable desire to spread us a lot of pills. If they want to cram too many pills down people's throat then more power to them. Their develops in business a bias, partiality and will to heed the owner or he or she who has the most say in the industry and not care about the consumer and/or patient of what they are peddling. All the time business even after they know they are in err with a useless good or service keep selling it and the rest of this same business get in line behind them. The "special people to please" the owner or who runs the industry have the most say whether the good or service that they are peddling us is in order and ethical or not!

So now who is the one that is delusional those that don't get in line behind the will of business or those who don't get in line behind a "principle" that say don't cheat, mistreat, or rip-off the consumer! Well now if it is me who is answering this question I am going to say that who is sick in the head is he or she who rips us off instead of adhere to the principles of safety and fairness to the consumer and the general public, ir-regardless of the will of the "special people" namely business and the political leaders on their side exclusively! Be fair and objective about the quality and use value of the good or service that they render and treat the individual consumer right accordingly is what I say! The people count more than the unscrupulous, unfair attitude of business and he or she that lives in good conscience and does the right thing by others is who is sane and happy and the others are not! Maybe they live in conflict withers that need not be and have no peace of mind! And live the lie that the special people and unfairness if that's what it takes for prosperity is what it is!

Example 91 "Environmental Shock!"

In the next chapter, ch.3, called Developing A Fuller Meaning To the Behavior Of Others I make a hypothesis up that declares that there is really stage of psychological development that all young people go thru, usually in their late teens and early twenties; they are waking up their mind to experience more potential meaning to the behavior of others in everyday life and are at the same time developing a fuller meaning to the larger processes that make whole society click- everything else in the overall culture, and that includes the government or other institutions like the church or various political clubs.

When a young person looks around to see what is going on right in front of him or her, instead of just noticing what others are literally doing in itself right in front of them they may see a second meaning coming alive to this same behavior. Why they may think that with this same particular behavior just exhibited by them that they are really trying to send them a message this way in the form of a hint innuendo, insinuation or pun using body language and/or symbolic communication intended for them to pick up on.

And when they analyze all of the potential meaning to the behavior of others they may began to take more notice to what culture or club, or other institution that this same particular person maybe affiliated with. Who do these people identify and associate with beside their friends at work. How does this affect what their political, religious, and lifestyle outlooks that may be different than just what you yourself believe?

Well now what does this kind of thinking on the part of someone that is going thru a phase or stage of psychological development where they are noticing a fuller meaning to what others are doing or believe in that they did not prior notice? Well just think about it, just because it appears someone is trying to communicate to you symbolically with what they are doing literally doing right in front of you let's say does that mean that this is necessarily the case or perhaps just a runaway imagination on your part? And when we are assessing what culture others are influenced by isn't their room for err in deciding what it then tells you about others? Might stereotyping and attribution take over that give a false impression of what this person believes or is about that we should consider, so that we do not fall prey to it?!

Delusion is real, but not necessarily incurable, because we can focus on being more careful not to jump to false conclusions about others based on just an appearance or gossip. We should learn to be fully rational in how we assess the meaning other behavior or beliefs instead of get carried away with false emotion! Look we've all been there with delusion thinking that others are against us when it is not true, but we can learn to see thru what is a hoax to our head...!

Example 92 "Environmental Shock- Does This Tell Us The Cause Of Schizophrenia?!"

As I have already proclaimed there is a phase and stage of psychological development that all young people go thru that I like to refer to as "environmental shock!" What happens during the environmental shock stage of psychological development is that we began to see the behavior of others on a higher order. And during this stage of psychological development we are beginning to wake up to a fuller meaning to the behavior of others right in front of us, and also compare at the same time our cultural, political, and religious differences that we may mark as important to be aware of.

But now schizophrenia is delusion and what delusion entails is that we believe something that is false with subjective passion even after we have already been given superior evidence to the contrary. Now there is no doubt in my mind that "environmental shock" is a major contributing factor for why people steer their boat into the mud with delusion. **If during the stage of psychological development that "environment shock entails gets us to see double meanings to what others are doing right in front of us or we are analyzing in a fuller way the potential influence of social groups and society at large we may misconstrue what this really tells us just because we are young and naive both.**

aturn

But now this does not begin to tell us all of the many factors or triggers behind schizophrenia. My point of view throughout this book is that schizophrenia can at least be treated by knowing all of the social, environmental and psychological factors for what is behind it, and not waiting around to see if a major biological factor exists also. Look not too long ago most people that were labeled schizophrenic would be put up in a state hospital for life. But now with the help of counseling and anti-psychotic drugs these same people can live a happy productive life in the free world. I maintain that the counseling in itself that goes on is crucial to helping one to gain confidence in the environment and situation that they find themselves in and overcome trauma from the past from someone that may have abused them in one way or another. Anti-psychotic drugs too, I will admit can relax people and at least keep them more consistently stable during times of crisis.

Example 93 The Biological Angle!

I will not rule out that there may be a biological explanation for better understanding schizophrenia, but by the same token I feel aturn strongly that it is really all of the changes that one is going thru in their late teens and early to mid- twenties that sometimes cause people to turn inward more than they should to develop psychosis in the form of schizophrenia or bi-polar. Look young people in their late teens and early twenties in most case are now working a full-time job that represents a new challenge and a potentially very stressful situation. (You see most people are not born enlightened but had to learn how to follow procedures like an adult on the job, and also how to interact with a broad range of people every day at work.) Most of them too by now are on their own by then, and learning to not only take care of the house cleaning, but also taking care of paying the bills too. All of this together, the adult working world and the fact they are now on their own represents an entirely new situation that they find themselves in. Just learning to communicate as adults for all situation including on the job can be really challenging. Sometimes trauma too that someone has experienced as a child too my inhibit one's personality, that keeps one from developing healthy interactions with others and this should be thought to include the vital kinds of communication on the job or personal business. All of these factors I believe help explain why someone might withdraw from others and turn inward to develop schizophrenia.

The proponents of those who still believe that schizophrenia has a biological cause point to the fact that schizophrenia seems to be passed along in your family tree, meaning that if there is a family history of schizophrenia from generation to generation then this points to the fact that schizophrenia may be understood genetically. That's right that schizophrenia could be said to be in your family gene pattern that is passed along!

The only other theory at all that seems to be being paid attention to that is biological is the fact that at least some people claim that the size of one' frontal lobes could have something to do with causing schizophrenia as at least some people in the scientific community that have studied this found a correlation between larger frontal lobes with the increased likelihood of acquiring schizophrenia. This is being debated though still and not a complete fact. All in all the proponents of schizophrenia have not offered anything substantial to believe that schizophrenia is biologically caused. They offer as a solution of course anti-psychotic pills which do not claim to cure schizophrenia but just can help stabilize their mood for the better. And when it comes down to it than we do not have a solution for rising above delusion and leaving this dreaded disorder behind like many of the proponents of the social, environmental, and psychological factors do have. It is those that believe that schizophrenia is triggered by stress that also end up having solutions to get one to rise above delusion altogether! This has been demonstrated time and time again as every day someone that is delusional rise above delusion that does not return to it simply by looking at themselves and facing their weaknesses, but growing in their ability to function like they should with others. Knowing all of the social, environmental and psychological factors in one's life and deciding that we want to do something positive about it can get one to come out of their shell and develop in their ability to get along with others better and overall function better out in the real world. Say a good amen for that!

Poor Julie took her pills regularly but from time still had bouts with the re-occurance of delusion. The pills made her relax better and put her in tranquil mood but they did not in themselves stop her from repeating in delusion, when facing the world with the right attitude and education on the nature of this disorder could help one to rise above it for good!

Example 94 Is Schizophrenia, Or Then Delusion Curable?

aturn

Well now I am an optimist that believes that anyone that is delusional can rise above that particular delusion and all other delusions along with it. Now isn't schizophrenia thought to be an incurable disorder in circles of conventionally accepted thinkers in this field? Well to that I would say that delusion which is the main sub-type of schizophrenia can be overcome entirely with the right coaching. We can indeed overcome delusion which if we do in effect have virtually overcome our schizophrenia. You know that it wasn't that long ago till most people that were really thought to be schizophrenic were put in mental hospitals for life. By now though with counseling available for the masses about this most people don't stay hospitalized but fortunately get to come back home after short stay, where many of them are living happy healthy constructive lives! Since Klaus Conrad a famous researcher on schizophrenia discovered that delusion is rationally understandable then we from then on have a climate of optimism all over the world that people can indeed overcome delusion and bask in the sunlight of the reality that the rest of us that are sane do. This optimism is shared by many of the psychiatric counselors on schizophrenia here or abroad in all honesty! If we can understand rationally why someone thought what they did that is a blatantly and obviously false to be the case then from there with the right support, coaching and education they will learn in time not to jump to false conclusions just because they are swayed by emotion and not reason or reasoning like we should be capable of. Although antipsychotic drugs in themselves may not get one to rise above delusion they can at least stabilize a person's mood who then with the right attitude can comeback in their right mind. Yes delusion can be risen above permanently, so then one is no longer really a schizophrenic. To keep repeating in delusion by now is becoming a thing of the past as many if not most who rise above delusion can learn to stay above it!

Jack Sandburg when he was twenty two yrs. old began to "see double" in what he witnessed when he looked around and seen others. Instead of just witnessing what literally in itself what they were doing, he began to also think about what the behavior implied potentially. That's right like others really may be trying to send him a message this way in the form of a hint, innuendo, insinuation or pun with what they literally are doing.

He now thought that others could be symbolically communicating to him with what they did that he had prior to that in his life mot paid any attention to. This caused him to at least sometimes jump to false conclusions about the meaning of the behavior of others. At least sometimes when he thought that others are trying to send a message to him using symbolic communication it was not true that they had. Jack got caught up in a guessing game about whether other behavior did or did not symbolize something beyond what they were literally doing in itself. It haunted him! It got on his nerves! And worst of all he was now believing sometimes that people were trying to pick on his nerves deliberately when it was just a runaway imagination on his part. He now could be said to have the delusion of reference and a persecution delusion that he did not have before because of this!

In the long-run Jack learned to be careful not to jump to false conclusions about the potential meaning of the behavior of others. He realized that he needed to stay fully rational and not let his uncalled for fears rule his mind! He also realized now too that if we are just a little bit more positive in how we treat others than delusion vanishes and the idea of a conspiracy from others goes away!

Example 95 A False Diagnosis Of Schizophrenia

Dorothy Ruiz, a renouned researcher on schizophrenia in an article called Some Diagnostic And Sociocultural Considerations claims that a false diagnosis of schizophrenia at least sometimes goes on. Ruiz highlights in this scholarly Journal that blacks for example can sometimes be diagnosed with schizophrenia when it is not really true. Ruiz also point out that when black are diagnosed by a white psychiatrist then a black psychologist that they are much more likely to be labeled a schizophrenic. Ruiz claims that blacks have a sub-culture of their own in many cases growing up and their inability to not adapt to their new roles in all ways in a white culture is definitely something to overcome. Three criteria is mentioned by Ruiz that may affect the diagnosis of a black person. 1) Cultural modes of expressing psychological distress; 2) racial factors in diagnosis and treatment of black mental patients; and 3) sociocultural factors and increase in psychotherapy.

Let's be sensitive to the true needs of each other! Let's be fair to everyone! Let's respect the rights of all of us including blacks!

Example 96 Games People Play

So what really constitutes a game to us in everyday life? Everything from someone driving in your way in the street that you presuppose is deliberate, to your girl-friend making excuses to you about why it is the case that she don't want to go out with you tonight? Everything from the gang at work teasing your nerves to your family trying to wreck you high-life because they were taught to run and hide from the rest of the

aturn

world? Everything from your best friend showing you that partisan politics means more to them than your friendship that you thought was solid and ir-regardless of politics, to the neighbors stopping to gauk at you every time you leave the house to go get a beer! NO one really likes to feel like they are being given a hard time more than their nerves can stand realistically and it is sad that people don't know when to knock off a game and be a friend! It is sad to report that delusion sometimes develops inside someone that feel rejection from others? Now who's fault is that? Well at least sometimes we did not reach out and show we love others enough for them to runaround instead of go into withdrawal and give up! May we love one another like we should even as Christ our savior has loved us!

Example 97   Action Oriented

    There is a Bible scripture that I like found in

◄ 2 Kings 5:14 ►
SUM PIC XRF DEV STU
Verse (Click for Chapter)
New International Version
So he went down and dipped himself in the Jordan seven times, as the man of God had told him, and his flesh was restored and became clean like that of a young boy.

    Now believe it or not I really believe that this scripture is a head's back mandate to establish that in the restlessness of our youth that if we want miracles to happen in our life we will have to follow thru many times in some cases to be become good at what we do. Young people are full of energy and are often restless too! A smart thing for a young person to do in this situation is to find something constructive to do in their free time and channel their restless compulsive behavior towards something that is also useful. Learning how to play an instrument can keep someone at home more. If one wants to be a good 10k runner it takes commitment land practice to become good at perhaps exercising every day over and over several times in one day just to lose the weight to be in shape enough to race. It might even look ludicrous for someone to practice that much, but altogether necessary in order to be competitive. And what about someone who wants to be good with cars or electronics does this not take a lot of time invested in actually working with these things to be good with it? Consider a young person that maybe goes out to his garage to work on cars two or even three time to be become the best mechanic in the town. Practice makes perfect!

People today run to the doctor if they have restless energy that they don't know what to do with. They in many cases suppress their urges to grow into what they could become thinking it takes way to much effort and practice with what they could aspire to by using an ability.

aturn

They take too many pills that they don't need that literally can stunt their ability to develop with what they could become.

Too many pills that stifle your "action oriented self" in your youth can be to believe a lie and delusion that their more aggressive oriented self was bad when if they just took their restless energy and channeled it constructively it would lead to a much happier more fulfilled self! Let's not suppress are impulses to use our abilities but act on them as much as realistically possible! Become a useful professional at what you do! God Bless You!

Example 98 Game Or Coincidence

How many times have we all had an experience where we were just sure in our own mind that someone staged a game to us when it then turns out not to be the case?! You thought that your family or friends are betraying you when it simply was not the case! You thought starting out at a new factory that the other co-workers were against you when there was nothing more false than that! You thought that the neighbors were in a sinister plan to get you in trouble over nothing that you did that was wrong! You thought too that the church and the

aturn

system had a sinister plan to wreck your life when nothing could be further from the truth. You thought that the car that drove in you're a way a little slower than you would like was doing so to be personally annoying to you when in reality the speed-limit for a few blocks was slower than you had assessed properly! You thought that the aggressive big black at work was trying to intimidate you and scare you when in reality he was just being friendly in his own way! You thought that the guy that lived next door was born without a heart of a spiritual kind, but then he fixed your car for you one Saturday for free when you needed it so desperately. You thought that the other neighbor was a crab, but once you got to know her she had been thru a rough life and wanted others to be more careful. You thought that you and your girl-friend were surely breaking up for good till she laid that kiss on you….!

Don't be quick to judge others; don't be quick to jump to false conclusions about them! May we learn patience tolerance and love for others that overrides uncalled for or hate. "Lord lift us up where we belong, where the eagles fly on a mountain high…,Lord lift us up where we belong above the world we know where the cold wind blows… " (Joe Cocker)

Example 99 Man I Am Tonight!

aturn

    I was twenty –one yrs. old when I finally said the sinner's prayer and really mean't it for the first time in my life. I became a changed person for the better. With the Love of God inside I began to grow at a much faster pace than what I just prior to this were doing. I had more zeal with my work ethic than ever before, and important than just that with me I also began to develop in my interpersonal with others at a much faster rate than I had been. I did not gain anything like perfection right away, but I soon did good enough to gain trust and respect from others.

    I had the joy of the Lord inside of me from then on no matter what happened. Even though I have not won great riches and honor among men I am quite proud of the self that I have become. I am still a winner and overcomer with God's love inside of me.

    I have not become an absolutely perfect person all the time, but I am awake by now and really on the ball to be help to others. Self-acceptance is a big part of making yourself a winner. A good attitude in every day makes for a winner too! To add love in your heart for others, and forget the past with God' help is something beautiful.

    I am going karaoke singing tonight, but all I can think about at the moment is that I am in my right mind and can accept the self that I have

aturn

become with Love inside for others. I have friends and I have the respect of others. I am happy!

I might sing the James Cohn song tonight Walking in Memphis! I like the words in

It that says, " ... tell me are you a Christian child? I said man I am tonight!"

It is to believe a lie or delusion that we cannot be a winner and have friends and respect too, but must go on losing in life. If we just add Love in our hearts for others we will come back into our right mind and be a winner if we stay a good attitude!

Example 100 Good Communication

Good communication between people ends potential misunderstanding in many cases. Consider the situation of a young person who is just learning a new job and trying to establish themselves as a good worker in whatever role they play. Learning a timely word on the job that may be work related communication, but not limited to it will sometimes change everything for the better. Suppose you did not know the rest of the gang where you first started working and you felt left out of what was going on between them in many cases. And let's suppose that you learned to speak up more to them for work communication or just to be friendly let's say. Whereas just a moment before you felt left in the dark about how to do the job most effectively and how to get along with others to 'the new communication" dispels the darkness and turns the light on about so many things. Potential fear, suspicion and not just plain ignorance about what is really going on around you can end just that fast sometimes.. "Yes", a timely word spoken between you and others can change the situation drastically. Any number of job related problems can end this way and getting along better with others can happen too.

As it pertains to delusional thinking that sometimes really characterized effectively the state of mind of a young person just starting out in the job market it can be delusional They may know not as good as others on the job and they could mistrust others, basically just because they do not know them and misjudge what they are about. They believe that others on the job are against them when is just lie of imagination. To learn to speak up in a timely moment and assert yourself can dispel the darkness about so many things that it helps dry up mistrust and just plain fear from not knowing the job or aturn the people that you work with. All of a sudden a world of fun, love and friendship can abound instead of feeling you are in the dark about everything! A whole new world takes over with effective communication that we need to have between ourselves and others! **Good communication does end delusion in many cases and brings about a dazzling beautiful experience where you are right in the middle of the fun instead of left in the dark!**

An interesting and useful article from Climb Professional Development and Training tells us that there are 7 benefits of effective Communication in personal and professional settings: "1. Building Trust 2. Preventing or resolving problems 3. Providing Clarity and direction 4. Creates better relationships 5. Increases engagement 6. Improves Productivity 7. Promotes team building." (Portland Community College)

Wow, Fantastic!

Chapter 3

aturn

Developing A Fuller Meaning To The Behavior Of Others:

Introduction:

   A short time ago in December 2018, I successfully completed a master's thesis on the topic of schizophrenia. The overall point of my masters was to "hip-up" the masses on what schizophrenia entails- which is of course delusion- so that we can better rise above it! Young people are delusional more than most people realize, where they sometimes in the fast lane of life- and in a hurry, jump to false conclusions about the true meaning of another's behavior. I now wish to explain how this could be said to be the case in this new book that I am writing: A Perspective On Schizophrenia that will attempt to explain how I believe it to be the case that all young people in their late teens to mid-twenties in most cases are really going thru a phase which should be considered to be a stage of psychological development where they are developing a potentially fuller meaning to the behavior of others than they once did at an earlier age. The

aturn

material for this chapter Is foremost a discussion of my theory that there is really a phase and stage of psychological development that all young people go thru I call environmental shock which helps explain why someone might become delusion. I am sixty two yrs. old and don't want to move away from my home In South Bend, In to do this, and also I don't really think I am willing to invest three yrs. of my time anyways in doing this when I can just give you the same information on schizophrenia in this book in a less ambiguous, but more straightforward and down to earth way that anyone can understand. My book is still a scholarly work that will include a rational basis for all of the crucial claims that I make in it. I hope you enjoy it and that it helps people to rise above delusion and see things as they truly are instead of being deceived by a falsehood!

"New opinions are always suspected, and usually opposed, without any other reason but because they are not common!"

John Locke

This theory that I came up with, namely that there is really a stage of psychological development that all young people go thru waking up their mind where they are hell bent-bent on understanding a fuller

aturn

meaning to behavior of others than they once did. It was my early thirties that I first tried to explain this theory. I have not found the right occasion till now to advance it in this book!

What Went On In Our Life From The Time We Were Born Up Until The Environmental Shock Stage Of Psychological Development Takes Over?

First what went on in the mind of kids from their early years on up to early adulthood? "How do we get from being newborns to being humans with "selves?

"Mead developed a specifically sociological theory of the path of development that all people go through, which he divided into stages aturn of increasing capacity for role play: the four **stages of child socialization**. During **the preparatory stage**, children are only capable of imitation: they have no ability to imagine how others see things. They copy the actions of people with whom they regularly interact, such as their mothers and fathers. A child's baby talk is a reflection of its inability to make an object of itself through which it can approach itself. This is followed by the play stage, during which children begin to imitate and take on roles that another person might have. Thus, children might try on a parent's point of view by acting out "grownup" behavior, like playing "dress up" and acting out the mom role, or talking on a toy telephone the way they see their father do. However, they are still not able to take on roles in a consistent and coherent manner. Role play is very fluid and transitory, and children flip in and out of roles easily:

During the **game stage**, children learn to consider several *specific* roles at the same time and how those roles interact with each other. They learn to understand interactions involving different people with a variety of purposes. They understand that role play in each situation involves following a consistent set of rules and expectations. For example, a child at this stage is likely to be aware of the different responsibilities of people in a restaurant who together make for a smooth dining experience (someone seats you, another takes your order, someone else cooks the food, while yet another person clears away dirty dishes).

Mead uses the example of a baseball game. At one point in the life of children they are simply unable to play an organized game like baseball. They do not "get it" that when they hit the ball they need to run, or that after their turn someone else gets a turn to bat. In order for baseball to work, the players not only have to know what the rules of the game are, and what their specific role in the game is (batter, catcher, first base, etc.), but simultaneously the role of every other player on the field. The players have to be able to anticipate the actions of others and adjust or orient their behavior accordingly.

Finally, children develop, understand, and learn the idea of the **generalized other**, the common behavioral expectations of general society. By this stage of development, an individual is able to internalize how he or she is viewed, not simply from now the perspective of specific others, but from the perspective of the generalized other or "organized community." Being able to guide one's actions according to the attitudes of the generalized other provides the basis of having a "self" in the sociological sense. This capacity defines the conditions of thinking, of language, and of society itself as the organization of complex cooperative processes and activities"

Young people 16 yrs. old or older perhaps now study educational material that focuses more on the expectation of the whole society may also work a part-time job where they are continuing to learn more about the expectations of the whole society in regards to what they do on the job that is then part of the generalized other stage of psychological development. Even though they have much to learn about the expectations of the whole society they are now entering this fourth stage of psychological development. This will continue on thru college and/or still early adulthood on the job role to learn yet more about the expectations for life related to what we are going to do for a living. Like they still may learn more about the laws and ethics and the diversity of the culture of this great land that will definitely broaden their understanding of the expectations of others in whatever role we play.

(Overall it will it take much further along age-wise before we have anything near a completely comprehensive picture of the expectation of the whole society including and especially all the laws but just to

aturn

accomplish a general understanding of the expectations of others on the job or the world becomes important for continued life.

About The Mid Teens: :

As a young person let's say in one's mid teen's one is a thrust towards more independence to be on your own and this precipitates more personal freedom, and in many cases includes experimentation with drugs and alcohol, or experimentation with sex. But In many cases a work-ethic in someone at this age or a constructive dimension is also developing sometimes the most as they may for example work a part-time job that teaches them responsibility and give them more choice by virtue of the fact that they can now go work as well as the increased pocket change from a part-time job. This should lead to developing into a more resourceful and useful self for the rest of their life. But now too those that really study in high school a believable amount and are quite good in academics will soon be developing skills that could make them a trained professional in that win scholarships and more choices in what college or university they will attend. These

aturn

too are becoming resourceful and useful for many tasks as well-even a professional high paying job sometimes follows. Practically everyone in high school needs to develop more comprehensive communication skills. If I were to characterize the style of most young people that are resourceful and out-going at high school age it would be that they may concentrate very hard with the physical or mental task in front of them, having not yet learned how important that guidance and teamwork with others in a bigger way must be learned to be more successful in life as adults. Good communication with a broader range of people than just your friends or a few, and not just diligence with the bare physical or mental work that it takes to do the task becomes essential for being a fully competent worker. As young people growing into adulthood coming from high school they will see the need for more comprehensive interactions to enhance teamwork with others, instead of thinking in a much more isolated way. Role playing at young adult age will begin to include in a big way the expectations of society in doing your role more efficiently.

aturn

Let's start this discussion with a preliminary understanding of what the identity crisis is about. An identity crisis is a developmental event that involves questioning their sense or place in this world. The concept originates of developmental psychologist Erik Erikson, who believed that the formation of identity was one of the most important conflicts that people face (May 28, 2021)

Next in article in Healthline written by Jamiee Elmer updated on Jan. 22,2019 we have an excellent description of the symptoms:

"Symptoms of an identity crisis:

Having an identity crisis isn't a diagnosable condition, so there aren't typical "symptoms," as with a cold or flu. Instead, here are the signs

You're questioning who you are — overall or with regards to a certain life aspect such as relationships, age, or career.

You're experiencing great personal conflict due to the questioning of who you are or your role in society.

Big changes have recently occurred that have affected your sense of self, such as a [divorce](#).

You're questioning things such as your values, spirituality, beliefs, interests, or career path that have a major impact on how you see yourself.

You're searching for more meaning, reason, or passion in your life.

It's completely normal to question who you are, especially since we change throughout our lives. However, when it begins to affect your daily thinking or functioning, you may be having a crisis of identity."

aturn

Solution To An Identity Crisis:

The obvious solution is to re-find yourself with a new identity that you like better and brings you more happiness and joy! So be it!

Creating A New Identity:

In our late teens and early twenties we are usually transitioning from high school graduation to our early college yrs., or even instead of college right away go get a full-time job and also live on your own by then too in many cases. As we introspect we are beginning to analyze all of our values from the past to what we are perceiving, experiencing, and believing about our self and what we believe right now as I continue on into a yet more mature adult. For example what do I really believe from the religion, politics, life-style of my past for what I now am beginning to see and believe for myself. What are the values of my parents in contrast to many of the new beliefs that I will be holding onto for my own including again my own exact lifestyle? This can be bothersome or even frightening trying to

aturn

realize a new value system our own instead just boing by what our parents and the system including education at an early age wanted us to believe and act. According to Jean-Paul Sartre "choices can be anguish" including what will be the full consequences. We may feel like a new self under construction and not just the product of our parents or family in general. We should feel now not like a subject of others but an independent free-will self, albeit there are certain basic values that should stay common to us alike. (For instance work, honesty and love…..) Life is still turning into our own existensialist free-will journey where our choices are more primarily our own now!

I will be making a set of values as an adult on my own that are different from the past! Who am I as an adult wherein I am still in the process of understanding the new self that I am discovering! What will become the values of my own as I develop a yet fuller self? And "yes" we are now starting to say to ourselves we are also now beginning to think about what the other guy or gal are up to that

aturn

relates back to myself? What are their cards? Are they potential competitors?

What Is "Environmental Shock" About?

Environmental shock should be understood to mean that we are experiencing a shock wave related to how we are now beginning to experience a fuller meaning to how we are experiencing the behavior of others particularly and foremost in the same environment in everyday life. The bottom-line to this is we are really beginning to understand the behavior of others on a higher order and it may change our perception of them till we re-adjust our mind to understand this better. Along the way as we are growing into a higher level of conscious awareness, we may have fears and doubts about ourselves,-growing pains- but if we just hang in there with a work ethic and maintain a good attitude towards others that we will emerge up the road victorious, with a much stronger character and more positive Attitude.

aturn

Nine Things That May Go Thru Our Mind While Going Thru Environmental Shock:

1) Fear or paranoia over feeling like you just might not be able to make it in the adult working world within the society.

2) The first of two really weird properties that govern the mind in a big way in early twenties is the experience of double meanings to what one sees that could make you think that others are trying to send you a message this way when it is just not the case. The second is the feeling that we are becoming like an actor on a stage giving a performance to others. Scopophobia or intense of being watched can

aturn

sometimes develop to at this juncture which can be kind of scary or at least angering to the person that is experiencing it! Fear that we are really being watched by others too when it is just not true sometimes takes over!

3) Stress that includes possibly trauma in our mind from the past. Healing the mind from these bad memories is something that we must do to better accept ourselves and get along better with others.

4) Spending too much time alone that can lead to delusion because we have not the proof of our thoughts right in front of us, but may believe whatever we might fantasize we think

is the case, or it has been drilled into our head from a bad source.

5) Delusion- we believe that which is not true about others, but cannot be persuaded easily to believe otherwise even in the face of overwhelming evidence to the contrary!

6) Complete lack of trust in others- this is where we no longer trust anybody but only our own thoughts that have already slipped out of reality

7) Psychiatric counselor or coach may be necessary-A. to help bring us back into our right mind again with sensible advice. B. the need for pills to prevent mood swings or curb delusional thinking. (Abilify is the best drug

that I know of for this. I recommend it strongly for schizophrenia or bipolar either one!)

8) Regaining confidence- delusion can be overcome even if it takes time to get back on our feet again psychologically.

9) A continuously good attitude- We need a good attitude towards others if we are to function in the long run efficiently! A work Ethic, Love and goodwill towards others is in order!

Entering the Environmental Shock Stage Of Psychological Development

aturn

When **the mind is no longer internalized just on how to work with the objects of one's labor successfully and how to communicate successfully with the bare minimum of communication needed to be accepted on the job, then the mind re-externalizes to focus on a fuller meaning to the behavior of others yet.**

At this juncture the environment that you are in comes alive in a new way that makes it look sometimes like you are observing a wild art exhibit of people in motion that are trying to send you a messages with their conduct that you now think you should be more of aware of. What really motivates others to do what they do?!

At this age we should be You should be realizing the need to acquire higher education which should significantly help your ability to pertains to understanding others in a much fuller way-- the society at large and all the fields of study that are relevant to it, including English, Philosophy, psychology, speech political science, history, and sociology!) This represents potentially knowing a much fuller meaning to others behavior in regards to you light of the laws, customs, and mores and ethics that we have

aturn

   As we continue to mature college education is extremely important for understanding the full meaning of other's behavior. At this age other's behavior can come alive with new in-depth meaning- to the behavior of others especially. What really motivates these people in all that they do and believe could be culturally or politically and ultimately psychologically influenced. We are better off with more education for understanding human relationships in everyday life throughout the whole society and the whole world. Are integrating our mind at a higher level of thought where we at psychologically and what we might do for a living the more education that we have that once again includes understanding of a broad range of people in our society we should then be better off that way!

   And now even with the influence of higher education at this age the mind can still get sick or lost sometimes along the way to one degree or another that we should be aware of. Again someone acquiring a more in-depth understanding to the behavior of others at this age may experience in everyday life, what I call "environmental shock". The mind can too easily get confused in how we should perceive and deal with others. One may develop paranoia,

aturn

scopophobia, social anxiety, panic attacks, delusion, or obsessive compulsive behavior along the way. For Example Potential double meanings to the meaning of others behavior or the feeling of becoming a stage act in all that they do in everyday life can absorb their thinking. Social anxiety or panic attacks sometime occur from stress on the job. Misunderstanding in how we construe the meaning of others behavior in relationship to us or then delusion can set in.   While the environment is coming alive to them in a new way they may really begin to feel intimidated by the actions of others, where it seems like others are expecting even a positive performance out of you. To borrow the words from an old Beatles song, "The wonderful magical mystery show is going to take you away. Going to take you away….what would you do if I sang out of tune, would you listen and try not to laugh, lend me your ears and I"ll sing you this song and I'll try not to sing out of tune….! These words from the Beatles, as far as I am concerned put into perspective how one feels at this "environmental shock' phase and stage of psychological development- like the pressure is on for all of us to perform better. They are going thru dramatic critical changes to how they think about others in a world with many demands! All eyes are upon them is the feeling they experience! The demands on them to be good students in higher education or on the job make them really feel like the pressure is on to do so. Their understanding of the world is expanding and hopefully it is not getting to scary or they are getting too shook by the changes they are experiencing, but instead find a way to adapt to the "new"! If their mind does get overwhelmed with unwarranted fear or suspicion they could really develop disorder! They will hopefully overcome this disorder as soon as possible! **We can all learn to overcome even delusion or others related disorders with education, treatment and a continually good attitude in everyday life!**

And now one more thing, instead of now relying on a biological explanation for schizophrenia that is inadequate because there probably is not one that is real, **I propose to put forward the pressing evidence that suggests that there are really social, environmental and psychological factors for sure that are a major influence in getting people to develop what becomes social anxiety and even delusion too that sometimes includes irrational thinking triggered by stress and/or general immaturity. Here lies a true and believable**

aturn

approach, perspective and analysis that is quite useful for better understanding the nature of delusion in order that one might rise above it also. By looking at the psychological, social and environmental factors for that help explain why we have become the way we are now. But now we can look squarely in the face our self that may need improvement in our understanding and sometimes attitude that may have led to this. We may have or had bad nerves and/or uncalled for overreaction or with draw from others because of trauma in our past that led to it. And then the too easily of giving up sometimes in our present circumstances, or simply the ignorance of not knowing how to act for some circumstances that we might find ourselves in. Learning constructive and useful interactions with others is a must! That in itself will help get us to more easily to rise above misunderstanding that sometimes leads to delusion. How much too we know in a particular field of learning- or about anything will determine our success at work or elsewhere we go. A biggee that can be a big plus to your advantage is the realization that you have many positive things to contribute to any situation which should include a strong work ethic and a good attitude towards others that includes manners and thoughtfulness that should

aturn

become part of our everyday will-power, commitment, and confidence. We ditch delusion by becoming a more competent knower and a better team-worker that will help get us to rise above delusion or social anxiety and become a superman doing real exploits with delusion vanishing!

What I know is that delusion can be overcome by facing our future straight on with boldness and the willingness to work and learn more about anything including a better understanding of our own self! I will stop short of saying that the social, environmental, and psychological factors are absolutely the only cause of schizophrenia but by being more aware of them with a positive plan to keep trying with a good attitude can indeed in the long run get us to be a success that ditches the immaturity of delusion for good friends and the joy of your real accomplishments.

I'll next present my roundabout support for this being the case in chapters 4,5,6,7, 8, 9, 10, 11, and 12 of this book. Then in chapters 13 thru 18 I give you yet more information, knowledge and advice about this particular disorder.

aturn

In chapter 4 Becoming A Stage Act In Everyday Life I talk about how we feel like we becoming a stage act. In Chapter 5 Caught Up In A World Of Symbolism I talk about double meanings to what one sees and hears In chapter 6 Reading The Signs Of Others Behavior I talk about reading the signs of others behavior right in front of you. In chapter 7 The Games People Play I talk about the games people play in life. In chapter 8 The Road I talk the road and the potential experiences that we have while out driving. In chapter 9 The Influence Of Trauma From The Past I talk about the effect that trauma has on our personality and outlook on life. In chapter 10 The Need For Employment, I talk about the need for employment to help us stay sane. In chapter 11 The Need For Literacy and Education In General I talk how literacy and knowledge can help us succeed better in everyday life including overcoming delusion. In chapter 12 I talk about how enlightenment helps us overcome delusion. In chapter 13 I talk about other disorder that can overlap with delusion. In chapter 14 I talk about how schizophrenia was treated by the system. In chapter 15 I talk about the past and present researchers of schizophrenia In chapter 16 I I talk about my diagram about delusion and the overall importance of it. In chapter 17 I discuss how education on

aturn

schizophrenia itself can lead a whole society full of people rising above it that would have succumb to it. In chapter 18 I discuss how a good attitude in general can help lead to one beating delusional thinking in general.

Chapter 4

Becoming An Actor On A Stage in Real Life Situations!

I believe it is the case that all young people that are waking up their mind go thru the experience of sometimes feeling like they are becoming a stage act performance in all that they do. Accompanying this you may in your mind's eye feel like all eyes are focused on your performance. Along with this you will also feel like the pressure is on to perform for the audience. William Shakespeare, the famous play-right once said, "All the world is a stage and we are the actors upon it." Then too Pythagorus apparently- the famous mathematician, also was a believer that when we wake up our mind that we become like

aturn

actors on a stage giving a stage performance. According to Wikipedia Pythagorus is quoted as saying, "This world was like a stage wherein many plays their parts; the lookers- on the sages...!" I believe both of these famous saying really gives true insight into how we began to experience reality as we grow up into an enlightened state of mind during environmental shock, namely that we could feel like we are becoming an actor on a stage in everyday life, or then we are putting on a performance for others to see. This occurs during this same phase and stage of psychological development that I refer to as "environmental shock" that I maintain all young people go thru- usually in their late teens or early to mid-twenties, as they are waking up their mind to acquire a fuller understanding of the meaning of other's behavior.

In the 1970's Erwin Goffman, (a very renouned thinker) wrote a best-selling book called "The Presentation Of Self In Everyday Life." This book confirms his belief too that somewhere along the way in life as we are still growing up even perfectly normal people may began to feel like an actor on a stage giving a performance in everyday life. In the introduction itself of this same book it gives one big hint for why

aturn

this might be the case! Goffman says in the introduction of this same book: "When the individual enters the process of others, they commonly seek to acquire information about him or to bring into play information about him already possessed. They will be interested in his general socio-economic status, his conception of his self, his attitude toward them, his competence, his trustworthiness, etc. Although some of this information seems to be sought almost as an end in itself, there are usually quite practical reasons for acquiring it. Information about the individual helps to define the situation, enabling others to know in advance what he will expect of them and what they may expect of him. Informed in these ways, the others will know how best to act in order to call forth a desired response from him." So then in other words when we get out there in the adult working world, full of professionals that we are going to feel at the very least like the pressure is on by others in everyday life and they expect a polished professional act out of you in your attempt to role playing.

Throughout the rest of this entire book Erwin Goffman is stressing the need to become a polished act or then professional in everything

aturn

that we do, if we want acceptance from others and complete success. As part of becoming a professional Goffman too stresses the need to be a good team player which includes flexibility when working with others! This is important according to Goffman. Make no mistake Goffman expects us to acquire the experience necessary in working with others to know the in's and out's of how to really become good to win in whatever roles we play in life. Again, throughout this book Goffman is focusing on the actual need for excellence in role playing itself.

In the case of those that might have abnormalities: scopophobia"- (or the abnormal fear of being watched by others) really think that in everyday life that just people from every direction are potentially spying on them let's say just to harass them when it is just a runaway imagination entirely. Just people in motion going about their own business in the same environment lead them to all kinds of crazy notions about them that are once again false. They may show a tendency to overact to what is really just people going about their own business but they think otherwise. The Scopophobic could be said to have fear of others in general that is not thought to be normal,

aturn

but paranoid. According to the Mayo Clinic paranoia is an unrealistic mistrust or a feeling of being persecuted. Extreme degrees may be a sign of mental illness! Also the scopophobic that also becomes delusional or schizophrenic in many cases may even think that they have been put in the movies behind their back by putting a camera on them that they cannot see at all and then showing it to others. They may feel like others in the same environment are doing any number of things right in front of them to put them on the spot and ultimately make a deliberate sideshow out of them. They may not always go incurably insane though, but in the long run come back in their right mind to realize that this was all just a runaway imagination on their part, and even turn into productive and mentally stable good citizens. (And if you think that I find this is funny that they have gone thru mental torment before they acquired a more truly competent understanding of the meaning of others behavior in the same environment in everyday life, this is not so. I say "hooray" for overcoming delusion and I'm your friend and not someone who thinks that's funny to see someone get hurt or sick out of misconstruing reality and having misunderstandings in the first place!

aturn

And now in defense of the scopophobic let's put ourselves in their shoes for just a moment. **Imagine in your early twenties walking down the street, and it seems like everyone is taking special notice of you.** At every fourth or fifth house that you passed on foot on this day you seen someone peering out the window or standing in the front yard of a house staring at you! What would you think? And if you seen someone standing in their yard making body gestures while looking your way, what would you think? That this same person is maybe trying to send you a message of some sort that is personal? And what if while you were still out walking you began to walk beside a road with major traffic. And now you see five cars drive by in a row that are all the color of white what would you think? And what if then you see a heavy-set guy driving the other way in a big fancy car that made him look like a "put the screws down guy" on you? What would you think? And finally while you were still walking on this same stretch of road you experience that at exactly every third intersection that you pass on foot that someone is crossing the road in a motor vehicle just as you are about to cross on foot with your right of way? What would you think?

aturn

The point of giving you far-wild description of what someone experienced while out for a walk is to make the point that just maybe those with scopophobia have are not altogether necessarily imagination that they did see what they did, but simply that they misconstrued its meaning. That's right it may be that they misunderstood even when having as good as a photographic memory to help them, but still not understand accurately the meaning of others behavior right in front of them which can be delusion! 'But couldn't this kind of misunderstanding happen to anyone? Yes, but it is most likely to occur with someone with scopophobia and paranoia already where they then let delusion take over too! **It is indeed though in general true that the naiviity of youth that is just not yet a good determiner of human nature to misconstrue the meaning of the behavior of just anybody repeatedly!** People that look out there window or stand in the yard looking around can be simply they are trying to protect themselves and their property from those who might steal or rape. And just maybe there will always be those that are out driving that at least sometimes capable of being discourteous to others in the road driving. The guy in the story out for a walk might be a perfectly honest and upstanding young man, but for sure a green

aturn

judge! **We all must learn patience, tolerance and a good attitude which will help us become more fully acceptable in how we construe the meaning of others behavior! Learning to be polite or even say "hi" to others sometimes can be very beneficial!**

Also as it pertains to the mentally ill, it is really people that suffer scopophobia (-or then have the fear of being watched) that complain sometimes that a camera is on them and that they then think they are being watched by others just like you possibly could in a play at school or even on TV. A real life confession from a man that apparently has experienced at least the start of scopophobia found in the publication Quora says, "It may be that you are beginning to experience a condition called paranoia. If you have actually been finding some of the hidden cameras you suspect to be in your environment, then maybe not. If you can find them, collect them and put them in a little box. Maybe the spy will in some way be exposed.

If you cannot find any hidden cameras, but still suspect their existence around you, stop, and try to reason this out. What is the basis of this belief? When did this belief first appear, and how did it come about?

aturn

Are you a politically active person living in a police state? Are you being stalked by an abuser?

Can you find any solid evidence that indicates that someone is spying on you? Is there any reason why someone else would be so interested in what you are doing that they would go to all that trouble?

Can you imagine yourself putting that much energy into spying on someone? Doesn't it seem like a terribly boring waste of time?

For most people, spying is a terribly boring thing to do, unless they are crazy abusers or they are trying to discover something very important involving crime or national security.

Are you committing big crimes or endangering a government somewhere? Is there a known stalker in your life?

If not, you probably have a false belief.

If this suspicion that you are being watched by means of hidden cameras cannot be justified on any evidence, nor dissuaded by lack of any evidence, you are likely falling into paranoia, and you would do very well to get some psychological counseling.

Counseling can help you find ways to release unnecessary fears such as those and to live with peace of mind."

A real life confession too from a woman that suffers scopophbia found In Quora publication also says, "I am not sure if this is what you are going through or are beginning to go through but I get so paranoid at times and I always feel like I am being watched and it worries me. I could be in a room with no one else and no windows and still feel I am being watched. I get paranoid and anxious and then my mind just starts to make it worse because I can't stop thinking about people being in the room with me and it is like a ripple effect that all started because I got paranoid and it kept going. I am always afraid someone is watching. I don't know why this started for myself personally but I know that it causes me a lot of trouble and that it can happen at any time for myself." (From Quora- a publication)

aturn

It is important to remember also that scopohobia, or the abnormal fear of being watched by others- even when it is not the case sometimes- that this then triggers the delusion of reference with accompanying paranoia, fear, suspicion and mistrust of others, that in turn might trigger the feeling that we are a stage act in front of others too I believe! Let me explain this!

Not only do they feel like they are being watched by others in the same environment, but beyond just that too, perhaps an audience as big as how many watch TV. At this same time they are assessing, (false assessing) the meaning of the behavior of others right in front of them to think the other person' behavior is related to them personally- to spy on them -or even make a comment to them with their presence. This particular issue is popular in rock-n- roll folklore. For instance like in the song by Michael Jackson, " I always feel like somebody is watching me: Like in the Hall-N- Oats song where it says, "Private Eyes are watching you…", or in the lyrics of the song by the Cars, "you think your in the movies" or also in "Who Can It Be Now" by Men At Work where there in lyric of it there is fear in someone that they could soon be taken away by authority just for wishing he had friends! Yet one more song by the Cars called Take On Me... In the part where it says

aturn

"you think you're in the movies, but I think that you're wild..." Is definitely alluding to a video girl-friend that obviously by virtue of the words in this song gets you to believe that she must no doubt be scopophobic, paranoid, and schizophrenic too that somehow leads her to believe that she is being watched by others in a big way when it may not be the case!

All these notions in these rock songs are obviously ridiculous, but by the same token quite common among young people and that is well documented!   Get organized with your head screwed on straight and see the world in a new and better way!

Chapter 5

Caught Up In A World Of Symbolism!

Introduction:

aturn

It is not always what we literally see in an object that we are observing that stands out to us the most, but what the object symbolizes to us. Suppose that a female that you look at smiles right at you in a way that you know that she is madly in love with you. This smile coming from this female to you then symbolizes or implies that she indeed loves you, whether this has been objectively substantiated or not. This of course constitutes a very common kind of example about symbolic meaning coming alive to you based on what you literally see. Now suppose also that you shake hands with whomever. This of course generally implies friendship or at least at least a civil attitude towards one another. And now if your standing on the top of the Rocky Mountains observing the vast beauty all around you; it may at the same time symbolize or imply the grandeur of a mountain; it may even symbolize the existence of God to you, with a feeling about the believed omnipotence and greatness of God coming alive that you right now feel right at this moment witnessing in nature! . And just singing the national anthem might immediately bring up thoughts of patriotic support for America- the freedom including all of the rights that we have. A walk thru the woods might symbolize simplicity and

aturn

peace of mind to you, instead of the feeling of the rat race that even a civil society with technology and its hurried up pace brings us.

    Not all symbolic meanings though that come alive to us will directly support something positive or neutral in terms of what it implies to you like the above, but negative symbolic meanings come alive to what we literally see too. For example (1) did you ever hear of the guy that was afraid to talk to women thought that women wearing slits in their jeans were sexually permiscuous when in reality the real reason they were wearing them is because they were too poor to afford a new pair of them or they were fans of Henry David Thoreau's literature in which he proclaimed "don't get tied up with a fashion contest but you're here to heed your higher calling of being a writer for example instead. Example (2) you ever hear about the woman that thought she was being stared at by men because she must have been a sex object to them when in reality they were just noticing the loud colors of clothes that she wore? Example (3) Did you ever hear about the guy on vacation seven states away from where he lived that thought someone that he saw with a red shirt on- which was the colors of his high school alma mater thought that this guy then must

aturn

be an alumni too from the same school? Example (4) Did you ever hear about the guy that because when she went shopping for him – that he noticed as she left she strut as she walked to the car that to him proved that she must be cheating on him when nothing could be further from the truth? Example (5) Their was this white guy that never trusted blacks intent in what they did because they did not talk to him much on the job when in reality the work on this particular assembly line that he was now working on takes the utmost of concentration to be excellent at it? This is sometimes associated with the particular state of mind that someone could be said to be in. Especially if one is feeling fear, doubt, suspicion, confusion, or hate in their thinking all the time this just might affect the reflection that comes from nature with symbolic meaning coming alive to what they see.

(A clarification to make right here and now it is important to keep in mind that (1) symbolic meanings to what we see does not necessarily mean that one is having a delusion. (2) And if we were to wonder whether someone was trying to send us a message related to that particular symbolic meaning coming alive to you that is not delusion in aturn itself. (3) And if we are to make an assumption related to what we see with symbolic meaning coming alive to us this is not necessarily delusion either. (4) One is having delusion when you believe the falsehood that others are trying to send you a negative message when there is superior evidence to the contrary.)

Next we need to keep in mind four terms that I will be using throughout this chapter and then throughout this entire book that are expedient for us to know. And they are: (1) symbol, (2) symbolic, (3) symbolic communication, and (4) subliminal persuasion. According to Wikipedia "a **symbol** is a mark, or a word that indicates, signifies, or is understood or represents an idea, object or relationship.." (2) According to Literary Devices **Symbolism** is the use of symbols to signify ideas and qualities, by giving them **symbolic** meanings that are different from their literal sense. **Symbolism** can take different forms. Generally, it is an object representing another, to give an entirely different meaning that is much deeper and more significant. (3) According to Wikipedia "**Symbolic communication** is the exchange of messages that change *a priori* expectation of events. Examples of this are modern communication technology and the exchange of information amongst animals. By referring to objects and ideas not present at the time of communication, a world of possibility is opened. In humans, this process has been compounded to result in the current state of modernity. A symbol is anything one says or does to describe something, and that something can have an array of many meanings. Once the symbols are learned by a particular group, that symbol stays intact with the object.[1] Symbolic communication includes gestures, body language and facial expressions, as well as vocal moans that Research argues that about 55% of all communication stems from nonverbal language.[2] Symbolic communication ranges from sign language to braille to tactile communication skills,"

Subliminal persuasion -"So, **subliminal persuasion** is simply influencing people at a level below their conscious recognition. It is influencing people with more than just words. It is the power of what lies behind or beneath the language. It makes use of the plain word's normal message in combination with a lower level of conscious cognition to effectively influence a person's decision-making or line of thinking. Some of the subliminal persuasion methods are influencing our stimulus

aturn

through smell, sight, sound, touch and taste."   (Social Media Today).

As I have already mentioned in chapter one the delusion of reference refers to how one perceives what is going on in the same environment. During a delusion of reference objects that are neutral come alive and that includes the behavior of others right in front of you with special meaning, in which you then could jump to the false conclusion that you are being sent a message by others when better evidence suggests otherwise.

As It Pertains To Delusion Of Reference In Particular:

As I have already stated in chapter one there are many kinds of delusion that one can have including the delusion of reference. The delusion of reference is the common kind of delusion along with the delusion of persecution. A delusion of reference is important to know and focus on especially since it is the most common. A delusion of aturn reference occurs when one looks around and notices special meaning to the behavior of others that falsifies a true understanding of what it is about. I will right now give you five different examples of how the delusion of reference could be said to come alive to illustrate how it with many ways that it does this. **Example # 1 colors:** Instead of just noticing literally in itself the color of a person's clothes or hair, you right then or simultaneously instantaneously thereafter in most cases realized not only just a **literal meaning** to what you were seeing, but also you realize a **symbolism (or symbolic meaning)** coming alive to you about what you are presently witnessing! In this hypothetical example some person was wearing clothes that are the same colors as your high school alma mater. You wonder is it also the case that this same person was trying to convey to others that they too support your alma mater as well, or is this just a coincidence that the colors that this guy had on were the same as them? Since it is the case that you are right now three states away from where you graduated just visiting relatives and this person you have never seen before, you think it is most certainly is coincidental and no symbolic communication of support for your high school was really going on.

aturn

Example 2: body language and movements: The body language or movement that one is using right in front of you, perhaps in what is imagined to be a hint, innuendo, insinuation, or pun to you on their part could even be said to possibly be symbolic communication from them to you. This of course includes the literal behavior itself that they are exhibiting add the special symbolic meaning that comes alive to you that relates to it. Does that mean that you are necessarily being sent a message by others? And if the boss at work in the same environment that is standing and staring at you with his or her hands on their hips might you guess that they wanted some expected work out of you soon? And if someone were to smile at you at work might that imply friendship? Well this of course is debatable, but one could indeed go ahead and jump to a conclusion that they were being sent a special meaning to you with what they were literally doing when it is just not the case. Sometimes in the fast lane of life so to speak it is fairly easy to make assumptions about the meaning of another's behavior when it turns out false. Delusion of course and not just an assumption is when there is better evidence to the contrary of what you may be thinking that should tip you that the symbolic communication that you think others could be trying to send

aturn

you is false. Girls have the right to smile if they want too without you knowing that it means anything significant to you at all. And the fact that the boss stands with his hands on his hips in front of you does not then necessarily mean that he is necessarily on the war path with the crew when this is really just his favorite position to stand in. (An overall generally negative attitude in someone toward others could get them to think any number of things about others, let's say based on what others are doing right in front of you that conveys a negative message to you when it is not true that any message was being sent to you at all by them. Their really frivolous in meaning behavior right in front you was really just a bazaar coincidence altogether! **Example #3 Presence** What is the relevance of just the presence itself of other particular people right in front of you? This could be said to symbolize some kind of hint or otherwise indirect message to you potentially. Perhaps the big boss that is coming thru your plant where you work, and of course this could be a hint to you to always keep things clean and orderly at your work station and stay busy or a pink slip is coming. Maybe though it wasn't really a planned visit for an inspection, but he was really in route to a particular assembly line near the one that you work on to witness on the assembly line next to the one you work on

aturn

to see how a new robot on this line is working. "oh I'm fine" you think. It turns out just the same that you were fired anyways though on this day for sluffing while this big boss was walking by you. You can't assume anything even when it is logical but not true. The guy was a real snake but you didn't think he would go that he would go that far under the circumstances. **Example #4 Martian Puns The obvious question is w**hat in the world is a Martian pun or double meaning to what one sees or hears either one? Martian double meanings does not focus just on any kind of double meaning to what one sees all by itself but it includes first looking at an object or person and then seeing right afterward turn to look elsewhere, and then looks at usually another person on the TV or elsewhere that presently has no real relationship to the first object that you first looked at. The acute correspondence of a symbolic meaning coming alive to it from the next object that you were looking at is shocking. . If you then were to believe that there was a real relationship between the first thing that you seen in regards to the symbolic meaning- and the possibility of symbolic communication being used this way could sometimes be absurd and delusional. To better understand this weird principle let me give you a particular example of a Martian pun that anyone could

aturn

have. Suppose that you were first in the kitchen talking to someone that told you that Fine-gold has the best car insurance. Then next you walk into the living room and on a comedy show where they were laughing together (having nothing to do with insurance and a guy is right then and there nodding his head yes at someone it would be absurd to think that someone on this comedy show were trying to send you a message subliminally to buy this insurance when it is just not the case, but delusional instead

Example # 5& 6 Post or Prior Delayed double meanings

A Bad Day IV- Post And Prior Double Meanings (or post and prior double meanings)   by Paul Johnson 1998

" Now in the last essay called A Bad Day III-Double Meanings, I explained how one can experience a symbolic meaning coming alive to what one is seeing in conjunction with their thoughts at precisely the same time or simultaneously a few second later (that had no prior connection and is usually frivolous in meaning)

Now in a Bad Day IV- the Post, and Prior Double Meanings I want to explain how it is possible to experience double meanings to what one

aturn

is thinking at an earlier or later time than when you observed the behavior of others wherein you acquired a special meaning to it.

Suppose that I had to write a paper for a magazine company that I wrote for, and the title of this essay I am to write is called Jock fanaticism in America! In this essay I inform the reader that since the 1970's it is not only the paid athletes that are taking care of their bodies, but now a large segment of the population- just anybody people, were now beginning to take care of their physical health. Long distance running was becoming a growing craze among the masses. Physical health fitness centers, where weight-lifting, aerobics, swimming, and basketball playing etc. went on, experienced an increase in attendance from the masses as more new health clubs were being built. People were beginning to really exercise like they should!

By the 1970's Arnold Schwarzenegger and Sylvester Stallone, a couple of jocks, were big box office hits at the movies. The Village People rock-n-roll band had such musical hits on the radio as YMCA and Macho Man. Richard Simmons had an aerobics exercise class show on TV that was on every morning during the week. Books galore were now being written on the care of your health by exercising more. Jock fanaticism was on!

aturn

And into the 1980's and 1990's the trend to exercise more continued, as more new health clubs kept springing up everywhere, and yes people were getting out of the house to exercise!

Now on the way home from the library after writing this essay, the post, prior, and reverse double meanings to what I wrote about began to come alive: I noticed a person jogging on the right side of the street almost immediately after taking off in the car that to me symbolized a high five gesture to what I had written about-jock fanaticism; also along the way driving home I noticed a guy standing on the sidewalk of a bridge facing the water and as I approached the bridge he began to drop down in a crouch position that to me symbolized an imitation of someone doing squats under a barbell; a little further up the road I noticed an elderly lady walking along the side of the road on the sidewalk with a sack of groceries in her arms, and the first thought that went thru my head was that she didn't look very safe in this neighborhood, when low and behold I noticed a rather big husky looking guy on a basketball court shooting hoop by himself. He was playing right next to where this lady was walking by when I guessed that it was probably a weight-lifter by the size of his large arms and chest. Then I thought oh this lady is safe for now with this guy close by.

aturn

It now stands out in my mind altogether how there could be said to be a symbolic interconnection between the article that you wrote earlier on, and then later what you witnessed in the behavior of others. You might say then that what you witnessed in the environment later was a "post double meaning" to what you wrote earlier on in this case. .

Then it is also possible to first observe the behavior of others and then write a song or story after the fact that in some weird way has symbolic meaning to what you witnessed in the environment "prior" to that.

Suppose that on the way home from work one day I noticed a guy with sun glasses entering a telephone booth to make a phone call. And a little further up the road I saw a girl laughing while being chased by a guy with a hose at a car-wash. Then further up the road I noticed no more females anywhere on the way home.

Well now when I got home I had an overpowering experience in my head of sadness that I missed my last girl-friend who dumped me for a salesman from Denver Colorado, but I still her when I think about her. So I wrote a song right then and there exclaiming: " I miss you, and I wish I could talk to you, you were so much fun and love, where have all the good girls gone now?!

aturn

And now after I wrote and sang out the words of this chorus in this song I thought of what happened prior to writing this song;-namely what I had witnessed on the way home. I thought to myself, gee it is as if these people were "cuing me with their behavior" or at least trying to "subliminally persuade" me what to then write about in my story?! Did indeed this "acting out a part" or at least "people in motion" somehow influence my sub-conscious? As far as I know what I just witnessed in the environment in the above story was just a coincidence, but the most overall relevant point that I want to establish here is that we can be subliminally persuaded or swayed in some way by what we see that affects what we think or do afterwards can be real. Again this would be an example of what we witnessed in the environment first or "prior" to what we then wrote about in this case." .(from The Happy Philosopher by Paul N. Johnson)

Now I have so far given examples of how one could notice symbolism in what one sees in the behavior of others or in nature alone: (1) how the colors of others clothes, or the colors in nature colors stand out to us with unique special meaning. (2) the body language and movements of others symbolize whatever (3) the presence itself of others, (4) Martian puns (5) delayed double

aturn

meanings I have just addressed to give you an indication of how the mind can be tricked into believing ta falsehood- namely that others are trying to communicate to them symbolically with whatever they are literally doing when there is superior evidence to the contrary that should get you to believe this instead.

Symbolic Communication Does Go On Of Course Though:

Not always is it the case that when you look around to see the full meaning of the behavior or others but even then symbolic communication could be going on. According to Wikipedia is the exchange of messages that change a priori expectations of events.

Now symbolic communication is where someone indeed communicates to others in a way that is not necessarily directly thru thru verbal language, but body language and body movements or even something that you wear to make a point about whatever!

Example 1: Then of course there is really communication for sure that is going on sometimes between people thru the use of symbolic

aturn

communication to others: Like when the pitcher gives hand signals to the catcher on what he will pitch. Obviously the pitcher's hand movements represent an actual language to the catcher of a kind in fact! So now if you think that when the pitcher makes hand gestures before he throws the ball that might include scratching his nose with his finger before he throws the ball this is really probably a signal, or z

Example 2 Someone wears red and white to symbolize that they are Southern California Trojan fan.

Example 3 The light house by the sea blinks its lights to a ship to keep it from running into the rocks or going back out to sea.

Anyways the overall point that I am trying to make here is that people really do sometimes attempt to communicate symbolically to others, whether it is to everyone with a message that is intended for all to focus on or it is a message sent to a particular individual that sometimes only that particular person might understand the symbolism to what is being implied deliberately with their behavior.

aturn

In the case of the schizophrenic though he or she in question usually has the tendency to jump to false conclusions about the intended meaning of others behavior wherein they think that they have been receiving messages from others when this is not the case at all. No one sent them a message at all with their behavior- they just imagined it. One could be living in the shadow of suspicion, fear, and doubt, and jumping to negative false conclusions about others. It is of course true that we all are capable of false conclusions sometimes where we have just made an assumption; and at least in some cases this could be a delusion too and not just an assumption if we know of better evidence to the contrary but still believe the falsehood!

Then too it is important to remember also that delusion in general of any kind is to believe something in reality that is not true about others that we should understand better, whether what we believe is based on what we witnessed in the same environment- or then a delusion or reference or a delusion of persecution, or what is going on behind your

aturn

back, or then the delusion of ESP. In either case delusion in general is potentially a very serious disorder that we should all be aware of that does go on sometimes in the mind of those with schizophrenia. What they misunderstand could hurt them or others.

(Part II Ralph Waldo Emerson on Symbolic Meaning Found In Nature)

Next we need to discuss Ralph Waldo Emerson that live a 170 yrs. ago and gave the most fabulous discussion of how nature symbolizes special meaning to us. That nature literally mirrors us a picture of many things including aestheticism, and virtue and vice found in man. It is really a heavy duty kind of Philosophy that proclaims that virtue and vices are real and that we as people are capable of either one. Next let's discuss in more detail his Philosophy of how nature has something to tell us that at least sometimes can be important about how nature mirrors a picture that can be thought to be frivolous up unto knowing the law of nature in your heart thru observing nature! Nature has many thing to tell us according to Ralph Waldo that

aturn

we should be aware of that I will now briefly try to give exposition to Ralph Waldo Emerson who believed that we had much to learn from nature:

First it is important to realize that Emerson thought that nature literally includes everything under the sun in creation including all of the plants and animals- including the human animal, man, plus dead matter too here on earth like the earth itself including the landscape consisting of mountains, valleys, flatlands and waterways too. In and essay called Nature, by Ralph Waldo Emerson, Emerson Says, "Philosophically considered the universe is composed of Nature and the Soul. Strictly speaking therefore all that is separate from us, all which Philosophy distinguishes as the Not Me, that is, both nature and art, all other men and my body, must be ranked under this name, Nature." (Nature, pg.2)

Second, Emerson believed that nature mirrors special meaning to us that goes beyond just literal understanding of the object itself, to what it could be said to symbolize for them. For Emerson nature mirrors a picture coming back to us with an endless variety of special meaning to it! For example the physical beauty of nature, that we can see with our naked eye, could be seen as being analogous, or then reflect back a picture thereby of the omnipotence of the incomprehensibility, unfathomability of God. The beauty of a landscape could be said to mirror a picture back of aestheticism that we then pick up on in the arts including writing, singing or dancing like where Kathren Lee Bates wrote America The Beautiful while standing on top of tall mountain in Colorado. "Every appearance in nature corresponds to some state of mind, and that state of mind can only be described by presenting that natural appearance as it picture. An enraged man is a lion a cunning man is a fox, a firm man is rock, a learned man is a torch. A lamb is innocence; a snake is subtle spite; flowers express to us the delicate affections. Light and darkness are our familiar expression for knowledge and ignorance; and heat for love. Visible distance behind and before us, is respectively our image of memory and hope." (Nature pg.17) .

Third, Ralph Waldo Emerson thought that it was marked by the tallness or smallness in man that reflects the existence of virtue or vice in man. Some behaviors in man support love harmony, and help in general for each other, while other behaviors in man sowed, sloth, ruin, and …, but man has the free will to choose between being big or small throughout life. Well now I am just sure that this heavy –duty kind of thinking about the laws of nature or the laws of God has much use value for us to be aware of! "Sensible objects conform to the premonitions of Reason and reflect the conscience. All things are moral; and in their boundless changes have an unceasing reference to spiritual nature. Therefore is nature glorious with form, color, and motion; that every globe in the remotest heaven, every chemical change from the rudest crystal up to the laws of life, every change of vegetation from the first principle of growth in the eye of a leaf, to the tropical forest and antediluvian coal mine, every animal function from the sponge up to Hercules, shall hint or **thunder to man the laws of right and wrong, and echo the Ten Commandments.**"

Fourth, the existence of virtue or vice can be found in man. Nobility and principle in action or virtuous behavior from people can be said to be virtue itself. "On the other hand, the hero fears not, that if withhold the avowal of a just and brave act, it will ego unwitnessed and unloved. One knows it –himself- and is pledged by it to sweetness of peace, and to nobleness of aim, which will prove to the end a better proclamation of it than the relating of the incident. Virtue is the adherence in action to the nature of things, and the nature of things makes it prevalent. It consists in a perpetual substitution of being for seeming- and with sublime propriety God is described as saying I Am." Pg. 168 Par 3

   Ralph Waldo Emersion definitely describes vice too- not with a hell fire and brimstone sermon along with it that I know of but sort of a chiding if you will of Small thinking instead of Big thinking for us, saying in effect that a small attitude full of vices does not reach or understand true progress or greatness. Vice itself according to Emerson can of course be described as complacency, sloth, a lust for travel instead of a love to make progress with our work for others, and to judging exclusively from a half negative point of view with gossip based on the appearances on the surface of a situation instead of a more optimistic and fully real way of understanding the same problems!' A passage that I just love from Emerson's Spiritual Laws that explains by way of example how we could overcome our smallness and be more virtuous. It says, if you visit your friend why need you apologize for not having visited him, and waste his time and deface your own act? Visit him now. Let him feel that the highest Love has come to see him, in thee its lowest organ.. Or why need you torment yourself and friend by secret self-reproaches that you have not assisted him or complimented him with gift and salutations hereto for? Be a gift and benediction. Shine with real light, and not with the borrowed reflection of gifts. Common men are apologies for men; they bow the head, they excuse themselves with prolix reasons, they accumulated appearance, because the substance is not." .

.

So what now does Emerson and the so-called laws of God have to do with Schizophrenia or delusion or mental illness in general?

Well now to be delusional in many cases can be said to be the result of too small an attitude to survive keeping our head above water! The world is a reflection of ourselves! If we see small-mindedness in ourselves we will also view the behavior of others negatively too. A good attitude about ourselves and others will make for a winner so whatever we are doing should reflect an image of a self that can accept-a self that we can be proud of. The virtuous person that comes from acting on good values is essential for being a winner. Emerson also talked about being a friend to other in every-day life that constitutes a good attitude towards others. . In Matthew chapter 5, Jesus preaches "the Be-attitudes" to the masses! Jesus Christ in this sermon tells us to have a good attitude toward others in all that we. Also I would like to mention a song of encouragement from Ray Stevens a contemporary comedian too that wrote a song called "Everything Is Beautiful" that also reinforces a good attitude: It says in it: "…Just take a little time to look on the good side my friend and straighten it out in your mind…!" A good attitude is everything no doubt!

.As far as I know Ralph Waldo Emerson never paid any special attention directly to the disorder or schizophrenia or mental illness in general that I am aware of, but again given I know that he emphasized virtues that constitutes a good attitude towards others. I am almost certain though that if he did directly help the nerves of the mentally handicapped-or all of us for that

aturn

matter that he would have emphasized more a higher love in man and the attainability of it for your own sanity just for one. . .

Part III Subliminal Persuasion In Advertisement

But now in this era a lot of TV is watched by a large segment of the population for long periods of time by the average American- whether they should be bothering to do this for their best physical and mental health of not! A couch potato is what America has become I'm afraid. But now relating TV to symbolic meaning and symbolic communication it is the commercial that give us a perfect example of how symbolism that is sometimes subliminal persuasion going on that is also trying to actually communicate a symbolic message to us about how their product is superior to their competition on the market. Within a commercial we get subliminal persuasion being used by business in almost all commercials to get you to buy their good or service. This is to send you a message at the subconscious level of your mind supposedly. Subliminal Persuasion is

aturn

potentially a powerful tool to persuade the audience that they have the good or service that you indeed really want to buy.

During the times of Ralph Waldo Emerson of the nineteenth century, the work day was usually much longer and walking was still the main source of transportation along with possibly horse and buggy There was no TV then! Today the average person watches as much as five or even six hours every day or almost every day, and there is a commercial that comes on every channel every few minutes throughout the complete broadcasting time in a 24 period of time of the station. It is a fast-paced world today more than ever before and "yes" advertisement for goods and services are offered by business on commercials. Commercials are of course intended to persuade the potential consumer with it that are attempting to persuade you to buy their particular good or service.

What Is Subliminal Persuasion

itself?

aturn

A very common technique to get people to buy their good or service in advertisement is to use **subliminal persuasion** in a commercial to get them to do so! What is **subliminal persuasion**?

subliminal persuasion

A self-help philosophy intended to increase the awareness of subliminal (i.e., below the level of consciousness) auditory and visual stimuli, and use them for behavior modification and as a therapy. Stimuli in the normal environment include white noise in the form of birds singing, traffic, pounding surf, rustling trees and conversation in a crowded room. In subliminal persuasion, positive messages can be dubbed into white noise as a means of deeply penetrating a person's subconscious, which may be successful in addiction (alcohol, drug, tobacco) disorders, pain relief and stress management. (The Free Dictionary by Farlax)

If we using subliminal persuasion in the commercial we are probably adding something unique to it that is in addition to what we would otherwise view or hear in it in order to persuade us at the sub-conscious level to buy it.. For example if I were attempting to persuade you to use my brand of drain opener in this commercial I might show the front label of the drain opener that I sell with a strong man flexing his muscles to imply that my product contains a robust drain cleaner that will really do the job. Another example of subliminal persuasion used in a commercial could be if we are attempting would be to make comparison between two products to get the bathroom cleaned. In the scene

aturn

where your competitors spray is being used in the bathroom the person is scrubbing for a long time but then when the good guy brand is used the cleaning takes not time at all and the consumer of this product is all smiles.

Stereotyping Is Used In Subliminal Persuasion

Subliminal persuasion in many cases uses stereotyping to enhance a picture of the superiority of their product over their competitor's product. Let's suppose that an attorney represented a drunk driver. This shister law firm won't pay the full amount of compensation they should for the accident to the persons hit by him in the wreck. This law firm is finally persuaded by the other side's attorneys- the good guys that they had better pay up or they are in big trouble! The use of stereotyping about crooks is not the only stereotyping that goes on to in advertisement about whatever but can also include stereotyping about race or sex too. (Not always but sometimes the stereotyping that a business uses about race or sex in particular gets called on the floor in

aturn

court for potentially offensive and harmful advertising. This happens from time to time!) Anyways stereotyping does indeed use advertisement to subliminally send you a message that their good or service is better than their competitor's good or service whether that is true or not!

Abstract

Scholars have long argued that popular consumer culture is both producer and product of social inequality, but few detailed empirical studies have explored the ways that advertising imagery simultaneously constructs stereotypes of race and gender. This article reports on a content analysis of television commercials ($n = 1699$) aired on programs with high ratings for specific target audiences from 1992 to 1994. Characters in the television commercials enjoy more prominence and exercise more authority if they are White or men. Logistic regression analyses indicate that images of romantic and domestic fulfillment also differ by race and gender, with women and Whites disproportionately shown in family settings and in cross-sex interactions. In general, 1990s television commercials tend to portray White men as powerful, white women as sex objects, African American men as aggressive, and African American women as inconsequential. The authors suggest that these commercial images contribute to the t exaggerating cultural differences and denying positive emouendotions. Results are discussed in relation to the segmentation of media markets and possibilities for social change.

The Effect Of Subliminal Persuasion In Advertisement Carried Over Into Everyday Life!

The effect of subliminal persuasion in advertisement on how we think the rest of the time as a result is real and should not be ignored!

aturn

The stereotyping too that sometimes goes on in commercials using subliminal persuasion can get us to dwell on stereotyping that goes on everywhere in everyday life.

Just like the commercials attempt to send us a message that we catch onto, if we are to watch them enough when we then observe the behavior of others in everyday life we may later on be scrutinizing what the potential message is to what you watch in the world at large. This notion to look for messages in the commercial carries over then into the real world too I believe to really be the case. What is the message I am being sent by others out in the real world all day too by it and not just the commercial on TV itself?

If we constantly think that others are trying to send us messages in everyday life, and it turns out there is superior evidence to the contrary this can then be said to sometimes be delusion! Delusion is real and affects us all negatively!

The obvious remedy would be to then stop watching too much TV and also consider showing better judgement in how we perceive and respond to hidden meanings or then "subliminal persuasion." Stereotyping in subliminal persuasion is of course potentially misleading about what others are really about. Let's acquire a true, and real understanding of others not based on stereotyping but use full objectivity and a heart in our analysis of them.

Part IV   Symbolic Interactionism

Now we need to talk about the concept of **Symbolic Interactionism.** Symbolic interactionism is about actual face-to-face interactions with others for deciding the true meaning of their behavior -and not based on the facts alone or the gossip that we have heard about others. According to Ashley Crossman, "…This perspective relies on the symbolic meaning that people build in the process of social interaction…" That's right, it is in our everyday face –to-face experiences with others that we develop our subjective beliefs about them. Example 1: Let's suppose that you have heard nothing but bad things about another person- "that this guy for instance was deranged and even crazy", but when you finally ended up working with him every day on the assembly line I realized that he indeed had a sense of humor about him that was occasionally slightly zany,

aturn

but he at the same time was bigger than others in his personality where he was tolerant more of others and even warm, kind and patient to all on the job. To you he was a great guy and not a crazy person to you at all! Example 2 There was this politician that had the reputation of being an unscrupulous crooked low down right winger. Like for the plight of labor he would insist that all if us that are poorl live more cheaply and not try to keep up with the rat race of inflation. I myself have a conscience and think too that the dollar and cents analysis of the cost of a business are real and how that if a business does not make profit like they come in business to do then they go back out of business. And if the business prospers then we will too….! I thought "I'll be wary of some of his politics though and labor should make a living wage as much as the business can realistically afford to give them…. and don't touch our social security to spend on defense…! Anyways my wife talked me into going to where he was making a speech because she personally wanted to hear what he had to say on the issues live! Anyways when you heard him live you got the feeling that he was really just realist and that he did love others including labor….and after his speech while shaking hands with the audience that he shook mine and invited me over for dinner and forget my troubles as a retiring union leader! Can you imagine someone that nice? Wow! I am now a crossover voter for this guy! Example 3: My wife invited one of her friends over for dinner! My wife had told me what a beautiful person this lady was as a human being and that she happened to be a professional singer too! Wow I thought I am looking forward to meeting this person! Anyways when she came over for supper she did not wish to talk politics with me but kept looking at my wife and talking the right dishes that someone should know in the kitchen. I thought she probably doesn't even understand all of the issues right in politics. And then instead of help my wife with the dishes after supper my mom had her stand in the living room and sing out-loud while I myself had to help my wife with the dishes. And when this lady sang it was all this dull "opera stuff"! I mean really boring! She was no Pat Benatar by any stretch of your imagination! Then while she was finally leaving my wife had her take the rest of the lemon pie that I wanted to for future dessert! Does this woman indeed have lack of moral scruples in such a way I thought! I mean she had no conscience or moral scruples- honest! To make a long story short after I now know my wife's friend

aturn

personally I do not going around saying anything bad about her, but that she just is not my kind of person to know for a personal friend and acquaintance. The end!

Example 4: There was this lady that was a very famous writer named Marjorie Rawlings whose book the Yearling I read and was influenced positively by. The other night I dreamed that I was out at the drugstore and ran into Marjorie Rawlings herself. I recognized her because she had been in a TV interview on TV not long before. Anyways I asked her if she were indeed Marjorie Rawlings herself and she smiled the most beautiful and loving smile, and said "yes"! With tears welling up in my eyes I told her how much I enjoyed reading the Yearling that she wrote.. I told her too that I quit shooting birds with the BB gun that I did at eleven and twelve: but after reading the Yearling at thirteen I never shot one again. I said, "you, are a humane, kind, and noble human being!" To which she said back very cordially, "Well thank you, your compliment means much to me! God Bless you young man!"

Example 5: There was this guy that was an auto mechanic that was a Christian named Bert that was talked about behind his

aturn

back like he were incompetent and hair brained in all his ways. He did swell back yard mechanic work for others though. He helped me fix my old Chevrolet many times and he loved the Lord and would ask me if I'm staying close to Jesus! I'd grin and say to him that I needed to get the car fixed, but I know what old fashioned, Christian, and brotherly love is even if I'm not perfect. He would then tell me to stay out of the booze and finish my car for free sometimes! I never had a friend like Bert! Love is real. Salvation is not an act but a reality that we have found our heart and conscience again and show it by loving others in everyday life. God is love!

   Anyways I hope these five examples illustrating how we are impressed with others will be different then just to believe what you were told about them that lead from the concept of symbolic interactionism I hoped you enjoyed!

   Furthermore I would like to emphasis that it pertains to symbolic interactionism to me it is the experience of people taking action while mingling with other people. One aspect of this is from Blumer's direct mechanical analysis of symbolic interactionism in which he proclaims that "Yes indeed" we could be influenced by the effect of the outcome of social interaction with others. In other words if we are action oriented and interact first had with others many times as opposed to have never met them this will no doubt potentially change the outcome of what we then think about this person. If we just sit back to learn just some of the facts or gossip about whatever this at least is sometimes going to change the outcome in a way that could be not as good as if you were right with the person in question in our mind. A hug between two leaders of a country after a diplomatic meeting could prevent a war! To visit an orphanage in Africa and see poverty right in front of you just might change your mind to care more about giving to foreign missions!

(**A word of Caution:** knowing all of the most important facts about what someone is up to and perhaps with or without social interaction in itself will give the most accurate picture of the truth of others behavior. This in our era seems to be the most dominating point of view. For example if you want to know who is the best handyman the facts in the business rating and not a talk on the phone with this person that is the most trusted/ What is the track record of this person in question that is factual

aturn

and not potential deception with smiles and handshakes with others. That is not to say that social interaction with others could not be valuable to know more about others, but overwhelmingly the facts alone should stand by themselves for making final judgement about what others are about, but of course understanding social interactionism properly is still useful for something in many cases..

Next, a brilliant student of George Mead was Herbert Blumer who did follow-up writing about Mead's theory of symbolic interactionism. Blumer's analysis zeros in on this in a way that stipulates three premises to this concept. The first premise tells us that, "human beings act toward things on the basis of the things that things have for them." The second premise is that the meanings of such things is derived from, or arises out of the social interaction that one has with one's fellows" "Yet the third premise is that these meanings are handled in, and modified through, an interpretive process used by the person in dealing with the things he encounters." .. "This process has two distinct steps. First the actor is interacting with himself the things toward which he is acting; he has to point out to himself the things that have meaning. Second by virtue of this process of communicating with himself, interpretation becomes a matter of handling meanings of others."

The next thing we need to know is what does this concept of symbolic interactionism actually have to do with a particular stage of psychological development that I call environmental shock? As it pertains to Symbolic interactionism this again is referring to the actual face-to face interactions with others that we experience in every-day life out in the real world at large. It is precisely when we are out in the real world in front of others that we are now noticing certain things about others behavior that we would not have otherwise noticed. f you remember with me in the concept of environmental shock young people are waking up their mind to a fuller meaning to the behavior of others in general then they once did at an earlier age. During environmental shock we are also noticing new things in particular on the potential symbolic meaning coming alive to others. Maybe others are to send you a message this way?

As you can see these two concepts have a similarity to them in that (1) they both pertain to the experience of being out somewhere in front of others. Symbolic interactionism wants to focus on how we experience interaction with particular others face to face and then impressed accordingly. Whereas environmental shock wants to focus on how we actually understand more in the behavior of others overall than we once did with anything going on in the same environment.. And (2) both symbolic interactionism and environment focus on how we are impressed with the particular meaning of others behavior right in front of you. For both of these concepts "What does it mean or imply in the behavior of others right in front of us.

And next what does both of these two concepts: symbolic interactionism and environment shock- (especially environmental shock) have to do with delusion or then schizophrenia? When its symbolic interactionism it could turn out that we are impressed with others behavior we are also deceived and then believe a falsehood based on appearance. With environmental shock we also could be impressed with others behavior in a way that deceives us into believing a falsehood. As it pertains to both symbolic interactionism or environmental shock either one if we are deceived by an appearance the facts should correct our thinking our thing unless we choose to believe appearance over facts. To do so would be to then be a delusion we have which is

aturn

the main sub-type of schizophrenia. Delusion of course is dangerous for many obvious reasons! To believe and act on a lie about others can be catastrophic to all!

Chapter 6

Reading The Signs Of Others Behavior:

Reading The Signs Of Others Behavior

The experience of noticing the particular indications of others behavior that appears to point to a message or tip from them whether it is positive or negative in. This can include highly imaginative and fanciful ways of thinking about what is going on that can sometimes lead to the delusion of reference or a persecution delusion in particular for example. This experience of reading the signs can be based on how we perceive a whole series of events in your day that make for one Big Picture of messages sent from others with a special meaning to it. When

aturn

we believe these special meanings to others behavior, when it is without a doubt false with better evidence against it, this is then an indication sometimes of one big reoccurring delusion with a perhaps one particular theme. For example others may seem like they want to scare you or others want to hurt your pride could be because the themes of continuing delusion on one sign after another in the behavior of others that made you think this. I happen to have written about this phenomena in a novel that I wrote call Schizophrenia Or Growing Pains. I wrote a passage in it wherein the lead character is remembering the events of six days in a row which was full of delusionl: "I close my eyes in the sun and begin to let my thoughts be whatever they want to be. I instantly have flashbacks concerning the experiences that I had all week where I at least thought that others are attempting to get under my skin with what they are doing right in front of me. Why I remember how on that on Monday when I drove to work how there was always exactly two unique motor vehicles driving out in front of me all of the way to work, and then all of the way back home again. I also remember on this same afternoon when I went out jogging that there were several drivers that had the front of their vehicle protruding out into the intersection directly in front of me. There was also several times when I seen what at least looked like the same female that I dated not too long ago now riding along with another guy in the traffic.

I remember how on Tuesday there was always exactly one motor vehicle out ahead of me on literally every road that I drove on all of the way to work and then all of the way home again. I remember how on this particular morning that their happened to be one particular female that was walking in front of me down the main aisle all of the way to the cafeteria on my break time. She was wearing a t-shirt with words on the back of it in capital letters that said MADD on it! I thought that she could be in collaboration with those in the street that drove ahead of me one at a time. The point that they could all be trying to make would be that the heat is on if I choose to drink!

I remember how on Wednesday I had numerous experiences where it at least seemed like others that were over-weight went out of their way deliberately by standing in front of me whenever I was in a line of people to get something to eat or drink. The message that I thought they might be trying to send me is that I

aturn

don't have the will power to stick to dieting plans. I also remember how on Wednesday when I went out running that once again like on Monday there was motor vehicles stopped with the front end of it out in front of me at the intersection. And just like on Monday there was several times when I see what at least looked like the same female that I dated not too long ago now riding along with another guy in he traffic. What a negative surprise to experience once again what is potentially harassment to me when I went out jogging!

I remember how on Thursday the fans of a particular rock band harassed me throughout out the day and evening too! Ew' what a horrid day!

I remember how on Friday that the live gig that I was supposed to get to play in did not happen. I also remember my thoughts later on this night how I could put into the framework of comedy many of the bad experiences that I had this week where I at least thought someone may be going out of their way to tease my head about whatever! I didn't find what they did comically amusing though!

I remember how on this day, which is Saturday, how along the

aturn

way driving home from work their happened to be a black sports car coming the other way in the traffic that really captured my attention. Sitting in the front seat of this vehicle happened to be what at least looked like this same female that I dated not too long ago now riding along with a guy that is driving this vehicle. And I remember how when I were out in the yard cutting the grass that I seen these same people drive by my house twice. I remember how after the second time that they drove by that I then accidentally shot an apple out the side of my mower into the side of the neighbor's house. I remember the verbal confrontation that followed with my neighbor after this happened!"

.

A Real Life Confession To Make:

I have a confession to make, and that is that I myself went thru an "environmental shock" myself from twenty two to twenty four years old.

I was literally caught up in a world of trying to analyze and understand the full meaning of the behavior of others –I was reading the signs of their behavior. Sometime I jumped to false

aturn

conclusions about the meaning of there behavior and interpreted it to mean that they were against me when it was not true. Overall in my head I was too cynical and judgmental about them inside. I would lash out at them verbally over trite matters, thinking that I was doing this because I had a sense of justice for all of us. At the same time I was inwardly full of fear, doubt, suspicion, and even confusion in making value judgments about others, and was fearful about what the system might do to me for not getting along with others like I should as of late. Little did I know for sure, but at least thought that I was just going thru a growing up phase that I might grow out of. Sure enough the sun came back out for me by twenty-five yrs. and I was not only getting along better with others again, but I was more confident in myself and more positive towards others. I had learned to become less judgmental about others in ways that I should not be. I was realizing that others are in situation too and seeing them more like they really are and now not judging them when I should not. I was building a bond of real love and friendship between myself and others like at an outa' sight pace! Yes brotherly love was in the air again for me and I had more clarity of thought now about others behavior or just anything! Thank

aturn

you Jesus for restoring my mind to a higher plateau and helping me to see others more like they are! They're beautiful people!

In the mean-time from twenty-two to twenty four I was mandated by the state to see a psychiatric counselor for my verbal temper and occasional conflict with others. It proved useful and help keep me following thru with my job especially. I have highlighted two visits to this doctor to give you an idea of what went on in the second one "the courage, the confidence, and the boldness!"

Pt. I "Facing up!"

Basically, the first several times I went to this doctor it was all about realizing and facing up to the fact that I right now at this point in my life had a problem getting along with other people that was unacceptable. He told me in no uncertain terms that I had to come to grips with my overboard temper and not getting along with others. He told me that I was taking things personal that were trite that I had better learn to overcome. He told me that unwarranted fear and suspicion about others when it was abnormal fear has no place in us! He said do not give up but go forward but be more sensitive and patient with others.

aturn

Remember that others count too just as much as ourselves and don't be quick to jump to false conclusions about others, especially when you hardly know them!

Pt. II "The courage, the confidence, and the boldness!"

After I had been going to this doctor for a while and improved somewhat in how I got along with others he shifted somewhat in what he emphasized in the discussions, attempting to instill continued confidence and zeal of going back to work for more. He told me that I should keep going with all of the constructive endeavors I participated in, and try to keep my sense of patience with people that got under my skin!

The Happy Signs Along The way Once We Wake Up!

Now once I went thru the metamorphis and adjustment that "environmental shock is, the signs or indications of the meaning of others was more loving among a broad range of people than they were prior to going thru environmental shock. I now could

aturn

make friends with almost anyone very quickly. The indications of others behavior included real love and not to resent each other Sympathy and trust, and goodwill abounded. Fear and suspicion that included paranoia vanished and more love for others was now present instead. When you know the real love was alive in me!

The What's Happening Games!

John Lennon wrote a song called "Mind games" that is a favorite of mine. I would like to right here and now put all the words of it in front of you and nickname it The What's Happening Games that depicts loving and digging each other with friendly intuition towards one another.

Verse 1]

We're playing those mind games together

Pushing the barrier, planting seed

Playing the mind guerilla

Chanting the mantra, "peace on Earth"

We all been playing those mind games forever

aturn

Some kind of Druid dude, lifting the veil

Doing the mind guerilla

Some call it magic, the search for the grail

[Bridge]

Love is the answer

And you know that, for sure

Love is the flower

You gotta let it, you gotta let it grow

[Verse 2]

So keep on playing those mind games together

Faith in the future, out of the now

You just can't beat on those mind guerillas

Absolute elsewhere, in the stones of your mind

Yeah, we're playing those mind games forever

Projecting our images in space and in time

[Bridge]

Yes is the answer

aturn

<u>And you know that for sure</u>

<u>Yes is surrender</u>

<u>You gotta let it, you gotta let it go</u>

[Verse 3]

So keep on playing those mind games together

Doing the ritual, dance in the sun

Millions of mind guerillas

<u>Putting their soul power to the karmic wheel</u>

Keep on playing those mind games forever

Raising the spirit of peace and love

Love!

[Outro]

Love!

<u>I want you to make love, not war</u>

I know you've heard it before

Finally I wish to also allude to a song by King Harvest that also talks about digging one another called Dancing In The Moonlight:

aturn

Toploader Lyrics

"Dancing In The Moonlight"
(originally by King Harvest)

We get it almost every night
When that moon is big and bright
It's a supernatural delight
Everybody's dancing in the moonlight

Everybody here is out of sight
They don't bark and they don't bite
They keep things loose they keep it tight
Everybody's dancing in the moonlight

Dancing in the moonlight
Everybody's feeling warm and bright
It's such a fine and natural sight
Everybody's dancing in the moonlight

We like our fun and we never fight
You can't dance and stay uptight
It's a supernatural delight
Everybody was dancing in the moonlight

Dancing in the moonlight
Everybody's feeling warm and bright
It's such a fine and natural sight
Everybody's dancing in the moonlight

We get in almost every night
And when that moon is big and bright
It's a supernatural delight
Everybody's dancing in the moonlight

Dancing in the moonlight
Everybody's feeling warm and bright
It's such a fine and natural sight
Everybody's dancing in the moonlight

aturn

No list of songs that discuss the "happy signs" possible would be complete without John Fogerty's "Lookin out my backdoor". Even the animals can alive with love if we are attentive to them. "Just got home from Illinois, lock the front door, oh boy!
Got to sit down, take a rest on the porch
Imagination sets in, pretty soon I'm singin'
Doo, doo, doo, lookin' out my back door

There's a giant doin' cartwheels, a statue wearin' high heels
Look at all the happy creatures dancin' on the lawn
Dinosaur Victrola, listenin' to Buck Owens
Doo, doo, doo, lookin' out my back door
Tambourines and elephants are playin' in the band
Won't you take a ride on the flyin' spoon? Dood-n-doo-doo
Wonderous apparition provided by magician
Doo, doo, doo, lookin' out my back door
Tambourines and elephants are playin' in the band
Won't you take a ride on the flyin' spoon? Dood-n-doo-doo
Bother me tomorrow, today I'll buy no sorrows
Doo, doo, doo, lookin' out my back door
Forward troubles Illinois, lock the front door, oh boy!
Look at all the happy creatures dancin' on the lawn
Bother me tomorrow, today I'll buy no sorrows
Doo, doo, doo, lookin' out my back door"
Source: Musixmatch
Songwriters: J. C. Fogerty

Finally I remember an episode of Regis Philman where towards the end of the show he looked straight ahead very directly at the camera with a big smile on his face and said, "**we've all been delusional!**"

Chapter 7   The Games People Play

aturn

Most of the "games" that people are thought to really play to others in life can be infinite and varied in nature and quantity. At least sometimes to refer to the particular action that is thought to be a game being played to others is really no such thing at all but just appears to be. I will elaborate on this distinction as this chapter progresses.

First let me list six different categories of different social arrangements of people which I thought up from which games could sometimes be said to be played to by them. They are (1) street crime (2) government (3) business (4) family (5) peers (6) and the traffic in the road. I will address briefly each category to get a quick idea about how one or more people in each of them just mentioned that will perpetrate some initiative that we at least think of as a game being played to others whether real or a delusion. .   .

First **Street crime** is a loose term for any criminal offense in a public place. (The difference between street crime and **white-collar crime** is that street crime is often violence that occurs in a public area whereas white-collar crime is non-violent crime conducted by governments or private industries for the purpose of financial gain. (Wikipedia)) As it pertains to street crime muggings robberies that sometimes includes murder to others goes on daily. In the case scenario of a someone that is about to rob a store let's say he or she is determined to get the money that is in the cash register at this time or they will literaly shoot with a t gun the store clerk. If you are a store clerk that is about to be robbed in this kind of situation it is no delusion whatsoever to take seriously like we should and try and protect our life and/or the lives of other innocent people from ahis potential robbery or even worse murder to you or others. Street crime is no joke as I remember the words of President George Herbert Bush in which he said that "we should feel sorry for the victim of crime and not the victimizer" which was in my opinion a very called for and appropriate thing to say.

Secondly government gets blamed for not only taking campaign money and using it for personal expenses, but also robbing other funds or making deals with business that are illegal to solidify the vote in an election. These of course would be examples of white collar crime by government officials which of course is bad and reprehensible when they really have occurred..

An example though instead of delusion concerning what someone mistakenly really believes about the government would be to think that the government is really spying on them and is trying to run their personal life based on the presence of postal trucks everywhere on a mail delivery day when they are everywhere you look when you are driving in the traffic. This of course is ludicrous and just not true even though it feels like to this person that the post office is a spy for the government with their presence everywhere.

Third, as it pertains to business a couple of white collar crimes that many businesses have been found guilty of is fraud wherein the business attempts to rate the value of the business and the company stock at a higher value than it is. Yet another white collar crime that business is sometimes found guilty of is money laundering in which money lets say from drug –peddling or other illegal means is put into a business that pumps up its worth that they then claim is from profit from the business.

A legitimate example of a complaint of the workers who work for a small company is that they do not make the wages that the high dollar workers in the automobile or steel industry. Now I want labor to get the best pay that a business can offer them, but not all businesses have the money that some big corporations have to pay extremely high wages! A business is in business to make profit and when the profit goes away the business goes back out of business! This is reality- not corruption, but delusion is what labor thinks when they are not receiving high enough wages to satisfy them when it's the case

aturn

business is giving them the best wages that they can. But of course too there is always the case scenario when labor should indeed strike for better wages because it is possible to give them, and in order! Just a class in micro-economics in college can be a great help to get just anybody to see the realities that business faces. Again each particular business has only so much money going thru their hands and when they no longer make a profit they go back out of business. Open-closed.

Fourth certain family members of a family are sometime guilty of murdering another family member or committing sexual violence against another family member or sexual crimes against them that is terrible, outrageous and very much against the law! Rationalizing murder, rape or child seduction is so very outrageous and unfair that I am outraged beyond words! There is no gray ground here but it is wrong, wrong, wrong altogether! And may you get caught by the state if you do!

Typically in a traditional values family at least sometimes parents, in the interest of making their kids be good, or to develop into a winner will restrict their conduct in one way or another. And that include who they hang out with, a curfew, or even stay at home in the house in the evening till the homework gets done. A quite common scenario of what happens is someone's family is they turn one of the family

aturn

members in for alcohol abuse or other kinds of drug abuse. Now how we look at this can be from the standpoint of the parents or the kid they are raising. From the parents standpoint they want to make winner of their son or daughter but from the kids standpoint they want more freedom including the right to make their own choices. Is mom or dad being too strict to them or kids a lot of times about to make dumn choices that need to be changed or at least guided by their parents till they get of legal age and no longer live with them. I like the song from Crosby, Stills, Nash, and Young called Teach Your Children well in which it advocates love for your parents and children both along the way. " It says teach your children well ... teach your parents well your father's hell we'll slowly go by, don't you ever ask them why if they told you would cry, but just look at them and sigh, and know they love you! ...!" And isn't it amazing though how if we have love for one another within the family that it makes forgiveness and working together possible. And that also prevents delusion or misunderstanding between the generations so that it is not now insurmountable! Hallelujiah for Love!

Fifth, your peers at work or elsewhere sometimes just might communicate to you by innuendo.to help or ridicule you either one. Take for example if you are overweight and all the guys in the department imitate how a large size guy walks around with his stomach out. But then even if they are trying to rub it I that you are over-weight maybe it because they really want you to lose weight yourself and be much happier that way.

Then what if your just new on an incentive job and your performance does not quite measure up to satisfactory in all ways yet but you attempting to get there. Well while you are still putting groceries on the shelf some of the other guys walk by your aisle eating a donut shortly before the shift ends to rub it in they don't have to help you on your aisle when they get done with their aisle;like they are trying to make you feel bad for not being perfect against the clock yet with your job yet. Then there is always another way to look at the same behavior by others and in the case of them walking by you eating a donut they are really just letting you know what you can get up too soon with a little more will-power and initiative on the job!

And then instead of rubbing it in games to you: your mistakes, character, flaws or whatever in perhaps not so nice a way sometimes they find for sure friendly ways to let you know they love and appreciate you. Like what if they on a bad day when you are not feeling too good but they still need you at work the other crew members helps you make it thru the day. And then what if on your

aturn

birthday they all find a special way to say I luv ya brother in a nice and friendly manner by all walking together down you aisle in a row singing happy birthday to you But then once again what if people at work just want to pick on your nerves in oh so many ways where you are sure that is it to hurt you for sure Like they are almost never friendly to you personally; like they walk far away from you when they are walking the other way down the aisle; they give their other friends snacks at work that they bring in but not you even though you work in the same department. Like they are trying to persecute you by rejecting you!

   No doubt your peers sometimes are capable of playing mind games to you, but hopefully for your sake they are not to cruel or thoughtless. And then what about you being said to have delusion sometimes if we really have a problem with everybody else. Like maybe we are misinterpreting or misconstruing the meaning of others behavior probably in a exaggerated and negative way. We all need to have a positive relationship with who we work with or hang out with instead of living in fear, doubt and confusion in regard to the true meaning of they're behavior. Goodwill and goodness towards one another overcomes with a good attitude can have a happy heart. Amen?! Amen!

aturn

Sixth, games people play in the traffic! If any place is gamey- it out in the streets! On some days it may appear that others out in the road are attempting to wreck you're day. Everything from one particular car driving out ahead of you everywhere you go real slow like to a whole row of cars out ahead of you on each road you turn on driving real slow. Well great ha'? That's just great! And what about how people can drive right up your rear end that stick to you like glue? And then what about the guy that drives up right beside you in the traffic and says explicate deleted to you and then speeds off? And one thing for sure I like my wide-open spaces in the road to enjoy a good day. I hope you're not of these bad people that want to wreck my good day, but a friend instead!

Now in all honesty it is at least possible that the other guy or girl out driving in the road too were really just converging and merging at the same place and time that you are coincidentally? I'm sure in fact that in many cases when we are quick to rush to judgement about the meaning of other drivers in the road that we are dead wrong sometimes! And whether people really play games to others or not it is our obligation to stay civil or we are definitely jeopardizing our driver's license. We all need to learn more patience, understanding, and tolerance towards other in the road also to be a good attitude out there.

aturn

What's wrong with common courtesy, manners and thoughtfulness out in the road once in a while and never road rage! Be courteous to others knowing that a driver's license is not a right but a priviledge by the State!

Chapter 8   The Road Again!

    Undoubtedly the road is a place that causes drivers to road rage by blowing some steam to the other guy right out-loud in the traffic; this panic attack may even continue when they get back home or wherever as they will continue to bitch out-loud about the traffic that they were just driving in.   Well can road raging lead to an arrest for it? The answer is yes it can! Yes it can! It is up to us to play be the rules of civility if we want to keep our license.

The Particulars About What makes

People Mad In The Road!

aturn

It is because people drive too slow in front of other people going way under the speed-limit in many cases. It can also be some turned right in front of you when you had the right of way! It could be too that someone could have changed lanes on you without signaling! It could be too that you at least think someone is stalking you because they seem to be following you for a long distance. It could be too you had to wait for a train. It could be that you are in a hurry more than you should be and that you are not mindful of the fact that others just happen to be converging in the road at the same approximate time and place you are which can be annoying if we let it be! Learn patience, tolerance, and common courteousness in the traffic by slowing down when we should for pedestrians and other slower moving traffic in the road. Other drivers that are properly licensed have just as much right to be out in the road as you if they are properly licensed for it. And if others occasionally really do make a mistake in the traffic they are not an infallible human being any more than you are is all that this proves overwhelmingly!

The Heat Is On!

aturn

I know that we suffer the institution of the police, whether it is uniformed or undercover police, to keep the peace, order, and safety! The police including the undercover police, fire department, and ambulance, are out there in the street to protect us all whether someone in crime likes this or not. They are not going away! It is you obligation to get out of the way for an identifiable police cruiser, fire truck, or ambulance on their way to an emergency! And if the police for whatever reason decides to pull you over, check you license and decide to ask you a few questions pertinent to what they pulled you over for it is your obligation to do so or you can be arrested for not doing so or resisting arrest too if that becomes necessary. Their job is not a joke! Remember that! It is life or death for all of us potentially to co-operate with them in the road when we should.

Can Road Rage be considered Delusional?

Road rage can definitely be considered delusion because we may think that others were trying to deliberately be annoying to you when

aturn

this is just not true. It may look out in the street sometimes like people really went out of their way to harass you, when in reality they were just people in motion like you, trying to go about their business in peace that coincidentally happened to cross paths along the way. Once again have the sense to realize that you need to be mindful to keep you cool in the traffic, being especially careful when it comes to pedestrians! If we cannot do this we may have a serious problem of staying civil towards others when it is our obligation to do so.

Moderate Use Of Alcohol Only!

One cannot expect to drive as safely with alcohol use than without it! Drunk driving causes wrecks and serious injury or even death to others or yourself! Drunk driving is rampant, but sometimes it gets caught and the consequences are not pleasant! You can lose your driving priviledges temporarily or for good as a result!

Driving A Motor Vehicle is A Priviledge And Not a Guaranteed Right! "The courts have

aturn

ruled that the safety of the public can overshadow the granting of the ability of the individual to drive. It is really for public safety that rules and laws are in place." (approved course) Driving is a priviledge and not a right: Driving is not a constitutional right. You get your license based on the skills you have and the rules you agree to follow.
(Drivers Ed.)

Chapter 9   The Influence of Trauma From The Past That Affects Our Present Behavior!

First of all what is trauma? According to Merriam-Webster dictionary, trauma is a disorganized psychic or behavioral state resulting from severe mental or emotional stress or physical injury.

Next we should be aware that there are three types of trauma: "(1) acute trauma- resulting from a single accident. (2) Chronic trauma- is repeated and prolonged such as domestic violence abuse.

aturn

(3) Complex trauma- is exposure to varied and multiple event of an invasive interpersonal nature"

Next what happens right after traumatic experience? "Traumatic stress can cause you to experience all kinds of difficult and surprising including shock, anger, and guilt. These emotions are normal reactions to loss of safety and security (as well as life, limb, and property,) that comes in the wake of disaster!"

How does trauma affect our future psychological state and self-development? "What experiences are traumatic, the pathways getting the most use are in response to the trauma; this reduces the formation of other pathways needed for cognitive delays, and impaired emotional regulation."

Next let me give you three major examples of real trauma that goes on in this world: (1) The first example is about acute trauma from a car wreck- There was this guy who used to drive just a little bit quick sometimes that could not stop for what had just had been a yellow light that slammed into the side of a bed of a truck that just began to proceed thru this same intersection at the cross street at the start of a green light. The driver of the pick-up truck, who was the

aturn

only one in the vehicle suffered whip lash that was minor, but nothing that very serious. The other guy who ran the red-light was tore up pretty bad. He was just about half unconscious when they brought him into the hospital and he was bleed profusely with a concussion, and his leg was seriously injured too during the wreck. Now in just two days after emergency surgery to his leg to fix a major break he was allowed to go home. He was put thru rigorous physical therapy for six weeks before he was allowed to return to work with certain health restrictions. He would never walk again without a cane as his leg was smashed hard into the floor of his car when he wrecked.

    Now as it pertains to the lasting psychological affect this wreck had on him he was extremely nervous to drive fast out in the road again and did not so. And from then on, on a four lane road or better got over in slowest moving lane. And from now on when he would approach intersections he would do so while driving much slower than he used to and always stopped at the intersection at the start of a yellow light. The negative side of his driving that come out of this trauma was the fact that he would get extremely nervous inside anytime an intersection was ahead of him for the rest of his life.

aturn

(2) The second example is about chronic trauma. There was a young man that was beaten to or three time a month for over a year before he had the nerve to squeal to the authorities about the continual beatings that he had taken from his step-dad. The authorities, after trying his father in law put him in jail for five years. In the meantime this kid finished high school living at the same residence, and then moved out on his own two and a half years before his step-father was to return back home. He never ever communicated to his step-dad again, but once. The lasting affect for a long time anyway was that he was more fearful of big guys like his father-in-law when he was around them at work or elsewhere.

(3) Finally the third and last made up example of trauma that I am addressing here is on complex trauma. This young man who was extremely close to his sister that was two years older than he was go carried away with full- fledged sex with her for about five or six times over a few weeks period of time before they both were so embarrassed and ashamed of themselves they never had sex again or anything close to it. The long lasting affect that this had on both of them was that they were embarrassed around others including even their close friends for years to come following. How they dealt with

aturn

this stress both of them was transcendence and self-acceptance of the mind thru religious experience The preacher said in a sermon that both of them heard that we can be forgiven of past mistakes in our lives and the memory of it. He said it was not to dwell even on who was the victim of trauma or the victimizer of trauma like to love and forgive ourselves and others too thru first clearing our conscience by asking God to forgive us and then we will live a victorious life to come! He said too that in Romans 8:10 that, "Therefore there is now no condemnation to them that are in Christ Jesus who walk now not after carnal principles any more but after the Spirit of God to be inside us now!" Both of these siblings also seen different psychiatric counselor in their twenties and were told that they should not and cannot live in the past if they are to be happy and a winner. A new attitude that is icthem by now were developing healthier interactions with others and maintaining a positive attitude knowing they counted just as much as anyone else and that they should learn to accept and respect themselves. What damage to their psychological health that caused them to avert or even resent and or not trust others over their past trauma was now being transcended! Praise God! The new man or

aturn

woman in them with an improved attitude was coming on to make them a winner!

What is PTSD?

According to the Mayo clinic, "Post traumatic Stress Disorder is a mental health condition that's triggered by a terrifying events, either experiencing it or witnessing it. Symptoms may include flashbacks, nightmares, and severe anxiety as well as uncontrollable thoughts about the mind."

About PTSD In Our Life: "Most people go through

traumatic events may have temporary difficulty adjusting and coping, but with time an good self-care they usually get better, if the symptoms get worse, last for months or years, and interfere with you day to day functioning, you may have PTSD, Getting effective after PTSD symptoms develop can be critical to reduce symptoms and improve function

aturn

Symptoms: Post traumatic stress disorder may start within one month of a traumatic event, but sometimes may not appear until years after the event. These symptoms cause in social or work situations and in relationships. They can also interfere with your ability to go about your normal daily tasks.

PTSD symptoms are generally grouped into four types: intrusive memories, avoidance, negative changes in thinking and in mood, and changes in physical and emotional reactions. Symptoms can vary over time and from person to person.

Intrusive Memories

Symptoms of intrusive memories may include:

Recurrent, unwarranted distressing memories of the traumatic event

Reliving the traumatic event as if it were happening again. (flashbacks)

Upsetting dreams or nightmares about the traumatic event

Severe emotional stress or physical reactions to something that reminds you of the traumatic event.

aturn

Avoidance

Symptoms of avoidance may include:

Trying to avoid thinking or talking about the event

Avoiding places, activities or people that reminds you of the traumatic event

Hopelessness about the future

Memory problems, including not remembering important aspects of the traumatic event

Difficulty experiencing positive emotions

Feeling detached from family and friends

Lack of interest in activities you once enjoyed

Difficulty maintaining close relationships

Feeling emotionally numb

Changes In Physical And Emotional Reactions

Symptoms of changes in physical and emotional reactions (also called arousal symptoms) may include

Being easily startled or frightened

Always being on guard for danger

aturn

Self-destructive behavior such as drinking too much or driving too fast

Trouble sleeping

Trouble concentrating

Irritability, angry outbursts or aggressive behavior

Overwhelming guilt or shame

For children 6 years or younger, symptoms may also include:

Re-enacting the event or aspects of the traumatic disorder thru play

Frightening dreams that may or may not include aspects of the traumatic event.

When To See The Doctor

If you are having disturbing thoughts and feelings for about a traumatic event for more than a month if they are severe or you are having trouble getting your life back under control talk to your doctor or a mental health professional: Getting treatment as soon as possible can help prevent PTSD symptoms from getting worse.

If Your Having Suicidal Thoughts

Call A Suicide Hotline Number!"

aturn

Trauma From Previous Lifetimes That Might Affect Our Ability To Think Like We Should Now! Can This Be Substantiated? Yes! (The Mind's Journal Written on Novermber 13, 2020 by Nanice Ellis)

"Most of know that unhealed emotional trauma can result in Post traumatic Stress Disorder PTSD, and many of us can carry unhealed emotional trauma from past lives?

In fact there's a different link between past life trauma and present day fears, phobias and panic attacks self your experiencing any of these conditions, you could be suffering from Post Traumatic Disorder.

What is past life Traumatic stress disorder?

Maybe you are wondering how you can carry unhealed emotional trauma from one life to the next?

Although you may live many lives and incarnate us very different characters, your soul remains with you from life to life, and even

aturn

though you may not remember a thing, your soul maintains the memories from all lifetimes and keeps track of unfinished business.

So each time that reincarnate, you take it with you, and this means that if you die with unhealed emotional wounds in one lifetime, you're born with the unhealed wounds in another.

Most of us have no memories of traumatic events that occurred in other lifetimes. Nonetheless when we carry unhealed past life trauma into our present life, it often manifests itself as some type of distressing issue that is somehow related to the original event.

When past life trauma surfaces through current life issues, it often triggers Past Life Traumatic Stress Disorder, and as a result, we might experience irrational fears, anxiety phobias, or panic attacks.

1. If you were ever severely punished for not following the rules in a past life, you may have an irrational fear of authority

2. If you were every rejected or abandoned in a past life, you may have an irrational fear ofs being different or not fitting in.s

3. If you were ever enslaved or imprisoned in a past life, you may have an irrational fear of losing freedom.

aturn

4. If you were ever excommunicated for voicing your beliefs or taking a stand in a past life, you could have a fear of being seen or heard (by the way, this is often the cause of public speaking phobias).

5. If you were ever killed by a ferocious animal or insect, you could have an irrational fear of certain animals or insects.

6. If you were accused of being a witch or burned at the stake for possessing psychic powers, you could have an irrational fear of being cold, and needless to say, this made long winters unbearable......Honestly, whenever I was cold, I would instantly into mild shock, and while I couldn.t think clearly, I felt like I was going to die,

How do we heal past life trauma past life regression and this means that under hypnosis they go back and remember lives where they experienced a particular trauma

Although this may sound somewhat "woo woo" I personally guided past life regressions for many years and the results were often astounding

aturn

Sometimes, first fear remembering past life trauma is not enough to heal it (for example my fear of the cold), but more often than not, healing is a process that must be actively embraced.

Therefore, if you ever want to heal past life trauma through a past life regression, remembering your past lives is just the beginning. This is why it's refutable past life regression throughout.

Who know how to work through a multitude of life trauma's.

Even though it might be interesting to remember who you were or what you experienced in one or more past lives, there's actually no need to remember past trauma life trauma in order to heal past life wounds."

aturn

Finally is the effect of traumatic experience really capable of causing delusional thinking in someone? The answer to that question is definitely "yes"! Thru credible research on this topic it has definitely been proven that there is in indeed a real connection between trauma and delusional thinking! Trauma hinders or hurt psychological growth including causing us to avert other or even hate others when we shouldn't be that way!

"We are told that "trauma" from our childhood plays an important role in making one fearful, or aversive because of a bad experience growing up with others. In (Ingo Shafer and Helen Fisher Childhood Trauma & Psychosis-What is the evidence?) "The evidence for an association between childhood trauma and psychosis is steadily

aturn

accumulate, and exploration of potential mechanistic pathways has begun. Emerging findings from longitudinal studies and demonstration of a dose--response relationship to others suggest a role of childhood trauma in the development of psychosis. The relative influence of other variables in this relationship, however, warrants further investigation. … More research is therefore needed to further develop and evaluate appropriate treatment for psychotic patients suffering from the consequences of childhood trauma. Nevertheless, the existing trials suggest that patients with psychotic disorders can benefit from both present-focused and trauma-focused treatments, despite severe symptoms, suicidal thinking, and vulnerability to hospitalizations.

Then too there is the stress and even potential trauma to what goes on right now with what you are presently experiencing- (which I have already mentioned in the list of potential causes of schizophrenia)."

Yet additionally another source that says that delusion is related to schizophrenia is found in Schizophrenic Bulletin- University of Maryland school of medicine which declares, "Twenty studies measured relationships between delusion severity and childhood trauma………… Meta-analysis revealed that delusion severity was aturn associated with trauma severity..." This quote represents from this article represents one more proof with a positive correlation between delusion and trauma. There is no doubt though that more research is necessary in order to establish an exact relationship between delusion and trauma." (And the evidence is definitely mounting with more new evidence almost every day for trauma in this life or perhaps a previous life.)

Then in Childhood Trauma &Psychosis an updated review by Pete Stanton, Brian Deniletosis, Brian Goodwin, Yael Davir it says, "Evidence for the association between childhood trauma and psychosis is well supported and continues to grow...."

In summary we can say that their indeed is proof of a relationship between trauma and delusion, whether it is the ultimate cause of it or not.

So then in some sense trauma can be seen as one major factor that helps brings delusional thinking! We of course want to transcend or then rise above trauma and delusion both! With the

aturn knowledge of what schizophrenia is really about plus help too perhaps from a trained professional on trauma itself plus a fully positive attitude to get better it shall be overcome!

Chapter 10 The Need for Employment

There is nothing that can sustain feelings of inferiority or lack of self-worth than to just sit around- all by yourself wasting time and not developing your work ethic like you should. Also to sit on our duff and not acquire employment can help lead to serious mental illness in many cases paranoia and social anxiety increases in this same person under these continued circumstances causing this same couch potato to turn inward and develop delusion and psychosis because of a false understanding of others. Everything from mild delusion that at least some would lock you out of employment if they could to a much more serious delusion of persecution that everyone perhaps is against them and they will not let he or she find ample employment; that there is a

aturn

sinister plan and that perhaps even up to violence is the solution because they see themselves as backed into a corner by others. This of course is terrible what being unemployed and spending too much time alone instead of participation with others in the world leads to! We may blame the women or the minorities or bisveresa in our head for our unemployment and lack of success when if we worked with these same people they would find overwhelmingly that these others that you were blaming in your mind are fine people to work with. So then continued participation in the world at large with others is helpful to prevent delusion and mental illness   If one is to become employed this leads in many cases to being a professional in what we do at work. **If one is to become employed this will help us to develop positive character traits like confidence , more boldness, stronger and more penetrating intelligence, team work, good communication, getting along with others and an overall better attitude towards others. . If someone gets a job instead of sitting around they will experience themselves and others that they will be working with in a more positive light that can help lead to much more happiness and prosperity. A positive attitude in someone that**

aturn

is working can and does make the difference between success and failure and a winner or loser.

In "Does Employment Promote Recovery? Meanings From Work Experience In People Diagnosed With Serious Mental Illness" A survey was taken- the results of which confirm that employment helps people recover from serious mental illness. It confirms that employment helps one to really overcome mental illness. "Employment has been highlighted as a determinant of health and as an essential milestone in the recovery process of people with serious mental illness." We need a strong work ethic along with employment to help us stay well psychologically! Let's get to work!

And the Need For Exercise Too

There was this man that perceived himself as a wimp and ninny simply because he did not have the gumption to exercise in his free time. His was sick in the head where he "did not believe in himself" like he should, but doubted his ability to be professionally good at all the things he did but was mediocre instead. He really lacked the mental "muscle of confidence" for the performance he should be aturn giving us! Then one day he put on his jogging pants and started going for a run in his off time five days a week. Well he lost fifty pound and really started to feel useful again! His attitude towards work and in everything else he really did improve significantly. His on the job performance and home life improved significantly. His wife and employer were over-joyed by the positive change in him. The end!

In "Autonomous Motivation And Quality Of Life As Predictors Of Physical Activity In Patients With Schizophrenia" even people with mental illness of schizophrenia showed signs of improvement in their attitude and behavior as a result of exercising. "There is clear evidence that proves the physical and psychological health benefits of physical activity (PA) in patients with schizophrenia. (Dauwan, Bgeman, Heringa, & Sommer,2016; Gorczynski & Faulkner, 2010.) Most people with schizophrenia-even those who are being work treated on a regular basis for it are still in the free world and many of them do work a job where to exercise in their off time would be beneficial to their psychological health!

Moderate Use Of Alcohol Only!

aturn

    In Understanding The Health Impact Of Alcohol Dependence, "Alcohol dependence is widespread among people of all ages and enormous health consequences. Alcohol dependence is a major cause of mortality and is associated with psychiatric consequences, neurologic, impairment, cardiovascular disease, liver disease, and malignant neoplasms. Psychiatric conditions associated with alcohol dependence include major depression, dysthymia, mania, hypomania, panic disorder, phobias, generalized anxiety disorder, personality disorders, any drug use disorder, and suicide. Psychiatric comorbidity, in turn, is associated with alcohol-related symptoms of greater severity. Excessive alcohol consumption causes brain damage, as evidenced by brain imaging, and related neurologic deficits, including impairment in working memory, cognitive processing of emotional signals, executive functions, visuospatial abilities and gait and balance."

    Now our overall physical and mental health including on the job or whatever else we are doing is contingent upon how much alcohol we consume on a regular basis! It is important that we are responsible drinkers if we are going to consume alcohol and not in excess! Be safe! Be conscientious about your future health!

Chapter 11 Lack Of Literacy And Education:

First of all let me say that literacy is essential to be fully competent in our society of today. Without literacy it would be extremely difficult to function anywhere like others.   If we can't read or write this would limit us in so many ways including job opportunities that without these two abilities this would heighten our likelihood to have confusion and misunderstandings with others- that could lead to an all-out clash with almost anyone. And could you imagine too the risk of an inferiority complex that includes misunderstanding the motives behind others actions or what is sometimes labeled delusion or schizophrenia. To not be literate is to not understand what is going on around you like others or then in other words be left out in the dark! Please, even if you have a physical or mental disability may you acquire literacy like you should be able to achieve like we should; It will open doors of employment that would not have happened and you might realize that others are not always against you but very much for you. We all

aturn

love you tremendously whomever you are and are routing for you to get the keys of knowledge that you should have! Oh God I pray we leave no one behind and in the dark without the basic literacy that we need including not only reading and writing itself but a basic level of understanding in more than one field of learning! This will really open our eyes!

It is a sad truth that mental illness is more prevalent in those with a low level of literacy than a higher one. The following is a sad truth in America and around the world: "People diagnosed with a mental illness are at higher risk of developing preventable chronic diseases; thus, health literacy improvements may have great potential to impact health outcomes for this typically underserved population. However, there is a dearth of research on health literacy of persons with severe mental illness. The purpose of this research was to investigate aspects of health literacy and identify factors associated with low literacy among adults with severe mental illness using three literacy assessment tools. Seventy-one adults with serious mental illness were assessed and a high proportion had limited literacy levels: 42 % with the Single Item Literacy Screener, 50 % with the Rapid Estimate of Adult Literacy in Medicine-Short Form, and 67 % with the Newest Vital Sign. Findings suggest that individuals with certain mental illnesses and lower functioning may have more difficulty understanding health information and have limited numerical literacy."

aturn

Anyways how lack of a higher level of education have to do with delusion?

Simply put if we do not get a higher education we may be more limited in our ability to do our job as efficiently and professionally as we should. We may be left out of knowing certain facts that give us more important insight; or overall improved analytical skills that may add more perspective in general on many things pertinent to the success of the job.

So how does the disparity of education make for delusion sometimes?

So very simply put I believe delusion, which is believing something that is false even after we have been given superior evidence to the contrary, thrives when no one knows the facts fully but only old familiar ways including the dogmas of religion or folk culture for instance!

Know the facts not the bullshit!

aturn

As we continue to grow up we need a higher level of competency in many fields of study. The more we know the better off we are job-wise and also the ability to function with more expertise at anything with an enriched state of mind! For example if we just stay in school thru high school and pass thru it successfully than we will have much greater job opportunity than if we did not do this.

"It is well established that adults who lack high school degrees are at an elevated risk of being on some form of public assistance. The largest literature pertains to welfare risk i.e. cash assistance to mothers what used to be the TANF program, and so we will use the cash assistance example to present our methodology."

So to acquire a real job then at all as a young adult that pays very much requires at the very least a high school diploma. Stay in school till you graduate if at all possible!

Can higher education really work to enhance an even more masterful understanding in whatever

aturn

field of study? "Yes", indeed more education past high school is vitally important for one to acquire to become fully competent in whatever field they may study! Even after kids have just graduated from high school, if they accomplish this, they are a long way away from being a competent know most of the time for roles that ordinarily require college education. This of course can change if they are to take college classes where they will of course learn the particular knowledge in whatever field of study that should then make infinitely smarter in whatever field of learning that one assimilates in college. As they take more classes not only in just one field of study, but even take classes in other fields of study this should enrich and expand tremendously what one knows about anything. As we are turning into a more competent knower thru assimilating education as we grow into a more enlightened state of mind overall as a result. We will acquire the book knowledge in college that we should about whatever that will lead to a professional role where we are competent far beyond what we would be if we had not gotten higher education in this field. .

aturn

(By the way, in order to turn up a grade at school I used to study even on the weekend at the library when others were probably drinking cold beer. I turned what would have been a C to a B or a B to an A by studying extra on the weekend like I needed to. This is a great way also to become a better competent knower in general in whatever you are taking at school instead of just haphazard learning. It is really this kind of commitment overall with studying in whatever particular subject that is crucial in order to develop a masterful understanding in the field. I myself was ill- prepared for college when I first started. I needed to know more in every field of study that I was to learn in including to develop a bigger vocabulary in general than I had for academics in order to be able to comprehend effectively like I should the subjects I was taking classes for. I too needed to develop my writing skills the college level that I had not practiced enough in high school with. This slowed me down and did not help boost my scores on tests or turn up a class grade to a better one! It was not until my senior year in college that I actually made the Dean's list at all for the entire academic year. So why am I telling you all this? Because you are going to want to be ready for the experience of formal education at the college level! Be prepared!)

aturn

Better Job Opportunity With A College Degree?

Yes, "Comparing the earnings gap upon graduation with the earnings gap 10 yrs. later out of school illustrates this. For the 1990's-2000's the entire initial gap was about 5,400, an in ten yrs. this gap has risen to about $26,800. Other analysis confirms that college start with higher education annual earnings is indicated by an initial earnings gap, and experience more rapid growth in earnings than members of their cohert with only a high school diploma."

There is no doubt then that the pay for those with a college diploma still get more pay for their job than just those with a high school diploma!

Chapter 12

The Need For Enlightenment

Enlightenment for our young people- (in fact everybody), should be thought to be an important but viable goal. Enlightenment for our purposes can be thought to be of course a very awake state of mind that includes clear comprehension and clear, full, sensible interactions with others using reason as a means for our guide in following procedures and reasoning intelligently about anything.. Young people of course are a "becoming" in how they do things at this age, meaning by that they are in the process of waking up their mind. They are under the process of self- discovery and self-development in general wherein they should be becoming a more intelligent, thoughtful, comprehensive, better organized person in how they approach life. The need for a more intelligent and comprehensive self as we become more holistic and fully comprehensive should mean major improvement for us in all that we do.

Why does the lack of enlightenment or a holistic mind make it much more likely for delusion to thrive?

Quite obviously the more awake that someone is psychologically the more likely that they will be able to stay ahead of other problems and that includes mental illness. Although I know of no exact statistic++ showing a correlation between mental illness and lack of enlightenment, it is definitely true that a more enlightened mind can much more easily overcome delusion and other disorders better because they are developing a self that sees and understands more in themselves and others as they are more awake than others.

Now Clear comprehension is going forward, and so forth, is the clear comprehension of non-delusion. The fact that it takes learning how to be enlightened and understand ourselves better-like how to be structured in all that we do is my guess to what this quip really implies. It would also be the ability to reason beyond just emotion by itself, but rationally also. Clear comprehension of non-delusion is the knowledge of reality and understanding ourselves better than to be delusional at all!

Let me next give you also a couple of viable reasons for why someone that is more fully enlightened will be able to better overcome or stay above delusion as a result: (1) Those that are truly enlightened are said to be more capable of self-acceptance and consequently are able to get along better with others as a result. If then one is also able to much more easily establish healthy relationships with others and then get along better with others than delusion, and mistrust between people vanish. 2) Those that are enlightened can see cause and effect much quicker in anything than someone who is not enlightened. The irrationality of delusion will very easily come to the forefront of your thoughts so you can more easily deiced then not to be irrational. if you are enlightened. One can very easily see quickly past the irrational and absurdness of delusion to much more easily rise above it!

It is a fact that those that are enlightened are more likely to show sound rational judgement in better understanding anything. And someone that is enlightened will be a much better judge of another's character than someone that is asleep psychologically. Someone that is enlightened also frequently shows more "called for" love and tolerance in many cases towards others than those who are not!

And by the way I am by no means supporting that we then go back to some big ado with a metaphor called the "delusional cloud" in Jasper's explanation of delusion that focuses just on the thought to be ambiguities of it and seeming unknowability of it. Enlightenment is the real solution to delusion and not prescribing too many pills for them that do not even cure delusion entirely. 1) Let's get to the realization that delusion can be understood and corrected altogether instead of just the temporary fix of pills! (2) Let's get to the overall solution of enlightenment too! I don't see enough people rising above delusion like they should permanently without being awake when they have had this sickness! And I don't have faith that even to the end of planet that they are really going to find a biological cause for schizophrenia!

William Shakespeare once told us "know thyself". If we can just come to understand fully the irrationality of delusion inside us- and what is behind it: realizing the social, environmental, and psychological factors behind it then we can much more easily rise above it. If we are awake enough we can all come to understand the irrationality of delusion in ourselves and overcome it because we understand ourselves well enough not to get tricked! For example if we were seeing double meanings to what we see or feeling like we are like an actor on a stage being scrutinized and trick your mind into believing a lie? Or did trauma in our youth hinder our personality later on in life? While we in actuality all want to be a competent knower with anything that we are confronted with- especially reality?! Don't

aturn

we want to be enlightened enough to see above and past delusion? Whereas many of the pills that people take for mental illness really stifle or stunt your chances to be up and going like you should be, and in your right mind! Pills-ugh! Instead of more of them than we should really take, learn not to be fooled into believing a lie that we will fully heal our mind by taking them! It takes staying resourceful and participating in the society with others too for delusion to fully go away. God Bless the whole world and may "enlightenment" be coming to us all!

Overall Summary Of Chapter 4 Thru 12

In chapter 3 I theorized that there is a phase which is really part of a stage of psychological development, in which the mind is seeking more meaning in the behavior others, that I call "Environmental Shock"! I claim that the mind get lost on false appearances of others, lack of confidence, and a lack of a positive attitude towards other or your own self. What follows in chapter 4 thru 12 that I will now summarize how this can be so and then show the glaring between self-

aturn

doubt and performance in relationship to others in the immediate environment around us foremost that I call "Environmental Shock"!

In chapter 4 Becoming A Stage Act In Everyday Life, simply the fact that those with scopophobia are seeking more meaning in the behavior of others in the same environment qualifies it to be directly speaking to be an experience of "Environmental Shock"! In chapter 5 Caught Up In A World Of Symbolism the double meanings to what one sees discussed usually begins in an investigation about the meaning of the behavior of others usually in the same environment. This focus of attention for those seeking to understand symbolic meaning in relationship to others also fits directly as a factor of support for the concept of Environmental Shock. In chapter 6 Reading The Signs Of Others Behavior, one is definitely seeking more meaning to the behavior of others usually in the same environment. This makes it a concept that relates directly to Environmental Shock. In chapter 7 The Games People Play definitely there is a focus on what is usually going on in the same environment, and then too can be used as a direct factor for confirming the existence of Environmental Shock. In chapter 8 The Road it is out in the road that people witness the driving habits

aturn

of others and what they think it then means! These experiences of how we perceive the meaning of others behavior directly relates to the concept of Environmental Shock! In Chapter 9 The Influence Of Trauma From The Past, it is a discussion of how trauma from our past affect our personality and outlook on life right now. Trauma is almost always experienced in the same environment that concerns an event from our past that is "traumatic" like an accident or being molested by someone else as a child. This indeed affects our personality and how well we get along with others in everyday life. The experience of Trauma indeed is support both directly and indirectly for the existence of Environmental Shock. In chapter 10 The Need For Employment it talks about how being employed can help significantly to get on to overcome serious mental illness! Of course we will still experience the everyday stress from the job and must learn to take of ourselves like we should. Being employed of course involves direct use of an environment with others almost certainly. Doing good work and getting along with others should be important to us if we are going to meet the challenge adequately. This too obviously be seen as strong support for the Environmental shock theory. In chapter 11 and 12 there may not be directly support for the theory of environment

aturn

shock, but both The Need For Education (ch 11) and The Need For Enlightenment (ch12) will influence how well we will perform in everyday life including while working that interrelates and confirms a relationship to how we handle environmental shock.

Chapter 13 Several Different Behavior Disorders That Can Become Delusional!

The following is an entire chapter that I wrote-most of which is in my master's thesis that proclaims that there are several behavior disorders other than just delusion itself that at least sometimes can interact with it. I think you should be aware of this fact because it is helpful in creating a more comprehensive of this disorder. I hope you enjoy it.

"Several Disorders that can Interrelate with Schizophrenia

Schizophrenia is a disorder! As I have already mentioned schizophrenia is a psychotic disorder that consists of at least two or more of the five most basic symptoms that we find within the schizophrenic spectrum for at least a month. These five symptoms that make up the schizophrenic spectrum once again include delusion, hallucination, disorganized, speech, disorganized behavior, and negative symptoms. There are in fact though other very particular specific "disorders" that sometimes interrelate and overlap with these five symptoms that are already established in the schizophrenic spectrum. They give us a broader perspective on what schizophrenia or psychosis in general could be said to sometimes include. They are paranoia, scopophobia, social anxiety, panic attacks, and obsessive compulsive behavior. I wish to address each one of these same disorders individually and tell you how they could sometimes be said to overlap with those five found in the original schizophrenic spectrum. I will then re-address hallucination and delusion to discuss individually one at a time along with these other disorders just mentioned, as they too both constitute a disorder in themselves, and also are a major factor for establishing the disorder of schizophrenia.

1. **Paranoia, or Paranoid Ideation**

First, I wish to discuss the concept of "paranoia" and "paranoid ideation." "Paranoia is a unfounded or exaggerated mistrust of others sometimes reaching delusional proportions" (Psychology Dictionary) The kind of fear that this entails can be said to be heightened and unnatural as opposed to being just everyday worrying about whatever. Then too there is the expression "paranoid ideation", which really too says something about the kind of unnatural fear that a paranoid-possesses, or paranoia in progress. Paranoid ideation is, "cognitive processes of continual suspicion and non-delusional beliefs of being persecuted, tormented, or treated in an unfair manner by other people." (Psychology Dictionary) This is in effect to believe that others are mistreating you. Paranoia or paranoid ideation is definitely a symptom of a paranoid schizophrenic. It is not difficult to see how the environment and the particular social arrangement there where you work, live, or commit leisure might be thought to interrelate with the kind of fears or suspicions that you might have. A friendlier environment of people might get one to feel more confident instead of one where you feel rejected and unloved by others, but sometimes one acquire paranoia or paranoid ideation to the point one is literally that way all the time no matter where they might be under any circumstances.

2. Scopophobia

Scopophobia is morbid fear of being stared at. (Medical Dictionary) Scopophobia is a unnatural fear that you have of being watched that can extend to a potential imagination that you are being observed from the other side of a camera- or even being stalked personally in the same environment that you presently find yourself in. This particular disorder is really a little bit more common than what someone might realize among the masses, as it is frequently joked about in rock folklore to the point that it says something about the common place of this disorder. In a popular song by Mike Jackson it says "I always feel like somebody's watching me stop playing tricks on me" I always feel like somebody's watching me, and I have no privacy. In a Hall-N-_Oats song it says, "private eyes their watching you they see your every move. Private eyes their watching you, watching you, watching you…." Yet in another song by Men At Work it says, "who can it be knockin' at my door, go away don't come round here no more…" Then too there is a song by the cars that goes, "You think you're in the movies, but I think that your wild-you might think I'm foolish all I want is you" Yet one more song by Paul Simon called Paranoia Blues- the chorus of which goes, "I've got the paranoia blues from knockin' around in New York city where they roll you for a nickel and they stick you for the extra dime. Anyway you choose you're bound to loose in New York City. Well I just go out in the nick of time. Well I just go out in the nick of time." (The last two songs just alluded to by Men at Work and by Paul Simon are both examples

aturn

of songs emphasize paranoia itself along with a scopophobic emphasis to it that people are really staring at you.

In literature too this theme of scopophobia also pops up. For example in Ernest Hemingway novels in particular several of Hemingway's characters could be said to have a scopophobic outlook or perspective on reality.

Another way to think about the existence of scopophobia among the masses is to also emphasize how it is the case that when one is scopophobic one also might feel like they are elevated to a "stage performance in what they do just in everyday life. According to William Shakespeare, the great play-right, "the world is like a stage and we are all the men and women of the play… the actors on it……." This is proof to me anyways that William Shakespeare himself thought that we could in fact perceive all our actions out in the real world as a stage act that where we are performer. Then too Erwin Goffman, a renowned thinker in psychology in the twentieth century also thought that our everyday actions that we commit out in the real world everyday could also be seen as a performance or stage act in which we are like performers on a stage. Goffman declares at the very opening of

aturn

his book The Presentation of Self In Everyday Life, in the introduction:

When an individual enters the presence of others, they commonly seek to acquire information about him or to bring into play information about him already possessed. They will be interested in his general socio-economic status, his conception of self, his attitudes toward them his competence, his trustworthiness, etc. Although some of this information seems to be quite practical reason for acquiring it. Information about the individual help to define the situation, enabling others to know in advance what he will expect of them and what they may expect of him. Informed in these ways, the others will know how best to act in order to call forth a desired response from him. …

In other words, the whole world can be our judge deciding how well we put on a performance for them in everyday life in all that we do. From there, it is not hard to see how young people experiencing a "scopophobic" state of mind, where it may feel like all eyes are upon you- may also feel like they are elevated to a stage performance in front of others in all that they do. It really may seem to this same person that a camera is on them and that really indeed are giving a stage performance to others.

aturn

(No doubt in some sense scopophobia obviously could be said to be environmentally related sometimes, but sometimes this fear is real for someone no matter where they go. To say that the environment or the social situation that they were in could be said to be related to the problem though definitely could be said to have potential viability.) There really happens to be no known cause for this disorder, but by virtue of the fact that a lot of people-even normal people, feel sometimes like a stage act one could theorize that it is really just part of a stage of psychological development that anyone that is enlightened has experienced along the way to one degree or another.

3. Social Anxiety

Next we need to consider "social anxiety". "Generally speaking social anxiety is the fear of being evaluated by others. Social anxiety is a "marked fear or anxiety about one or more social situations in which the individual is exposed to possible scrutiny by others. Examples include social interactions, being observed, and performing in front of others." (DSM-5, 2013,pp. 202) For example you could be said to have social anxiety if you are now working in a group situation of a now kind that requires a lot of work related communication toward your co-workers that you are having a difficulty delivering on due to past inhibitions in your interactions with others. Then too for an example you could be thrust into a situation at school where it is your job to deliver a speech when you have no practice speaking in front of a whole group of people and you are terribly reserved and shy in your communication with others.

It is important to remember that the presence of this disorder in someone does not then necessarily make this same person a schizophrenic too as this may be far from true. Many people have social anxiety that do not also have schizophrenia even though these two disorders could be said to sometimes interact with each other. And if for example one has extreme fear of others that is also accompanied by delusion or hallucination too then they then could possibly be said to be schizophrenic too.

4. **Panic Attacks**

Next we need to discuss panic attack or then panic disorder. Stated in the DSM-5:

A panic attack is an abrupt surge of intense fear or intense discomfort that reaches a peak within minutes, and during which time four or more of a list of 13 physical and cognitive symptoms occur. The symptoms of a panic attack include (1) Palpitations, pounding heart, or accelerated heart rate. (2) Sweating (3 Trembling or shaking. (4) Sensations of shortness of breath or smothering. (5) Feeling of choking. (6) Chest pain or discomfort. (7) Nausea or abdominal distress (8) Feeling dizzy, unsteady, light-headed, 0r faint. (9) Chills or heat sensations. (10) Paresthesias (numbing or tingling sensations. (11) Derealization (feelings of unreality) or depersonalization (being detached from oneself). (12) Fear of losing control or "going crazy." (13) Fear of dying. (DSM-5 2013 pp.208)

There is definitely too sometimes a connection between a panic attack, where you get emotionally shook-up about something, and then perhaps react with a fit of anger about whatever. Like the coach of a baseball or football team where when the coach think that a bad call has been made which will hurt his team's opportunity to win let's say that in an actual state of panic now coupled with anger he or she may bitch vehemently about the call in question right then and there. To yell out-loud about whatever that bothers you of course can sometimes be a manifestation of a panic attack that is possibly getting carried away. A drunken rage could too I suppose under certain circumstances be considered part of a panic attack too when fear and panic take over inside of someone. And as to whether this makes you a schizophrenic or not it definitely could be said to be going in that direction.

It is important to keep in mind that just because one has panic attacks does not then mean necessarily that this same person is schizophrenic, but this is quite possible. Anxiety, at the very least is definitely present when a panic attack occurs in someone. "Anxiety is considered an expected symptom of psychosis, which is accountable for psychotic disorders." (CHING-YEN, MD, CHIA-YIH LI, MD AND YONG-YI YANG MD, 2001, pp. 55) Then too there is definitely the possibility that delusion is going on in the mind of those that are easy to get angry; like they maybe are really misconstruing the general meaning or the overall purpose in the issue.

5. OCD or Obsessive Compulsive Disorder

Obsessive compulsive disorder includes the presence of obsessions and disorders both. Obsessions are: "Recurrent and persistent thoughts, urges, or images that are experienced, at some cause marked anxiety or distress." (DSM-5 2013, pp. 237) Compulsion is: "Repetitive behaviors (e.g., hand washing, ordering, checking, or mental act (e.g. praying, counting, repeating words silently) that the individual feels driven to perform in response to an obsession or according to rules that must be applied rigidly." (DSM-5 2013, pp. 237) Pace walking back and forth continuously or chain smoking everyday are no doubt examples of obsessive compulsive behavior. Without claiming to know for sure why people become an obsessive compulsive person beyond just to say that they at the same time suffering "addiction" to cigarettes, alcohol, or whatever. There is also sometimes a direct enough connection between do believe too in general that obsessive compulsive behavior many times has something to do with the wrestles-ness or wrestle-less energy that we may be said to have at a young age. This we can train ourselves to channel constructively. Believe it or not there is a much more potentially happy ending that can come out of wrestle- less energy when it is channeled constructively instead of for something pointless or negative. Let's imagine taking our wrest-less energy that we may have in our youth and instead of using it for something negative use it for something positive and see how much better this works for you. A classic example of this would be a young person that instead of chain smoking goes long distance running instead and sheds pounds and then wins a race too. What too about a young mechanic who instead of just sits in the house in the evening making one trip after the next to the refrigerator to get another and another and another beer he instead goes back out to the garage behind his houses after and becomes the best mechanic in the town? We can indeed learn to channel our wrestle – less energy constructively if we put our mind to it.

There is of course the possibility that our OCD is intertwined with delusional thinking that like a "bad habit" in itself is something not to like. If one's wrest-less energy is connected to an "obsession" that is "compulsive" that also is based on a "negative fantasy" that misconstrue a real picture of reality this could be dangerous and definitely be said to be a schizophrenic tendency then.

6. Hallucination

Next I wish to briefly discuss hallucination. As we have already discussed, "Hallucinations are sounds or other sensations experienced as real when they exist only in your mind." (Smith, M., and Segal, J., 2017, pp.4). Once again hallucination like delusion is directly speaking a schizo-type disorder. Hallucination is of course one of the five original symptoms of this Process disorder. Hallucination like delusion is a "major symptom" of this disorder sometimes, as it can take people out of reality as the rest of us understand it.

7. Delusion

aturn

Once again, "A delusion is a firmly held idea that person has despite clear and obvious evidence that it isn't true. Delusions are extremely common in schizophrenia, occurring in more than 90% of those who have the disorder. Often these delusions involve illogical or bizarre ideas or fantasies…" (Smith, M., and Segal, J., 2017, pp.4). Delusion is to believe with conviction that something is true, even when it is not and you have been presented with much better evidence to the contrary. Dorothy Ruiz, a prominent researcher on schizophrenia, says in effect that "**schizophrenia is delusion…**"! A quote directly from her says, "Schizophrenia is an illusive illness. The symptoms consists of **persecution** or **reference** not occurring in the context of severe depression;…" (Ruiz, D., 1982. pp 315)

(Two of the most common kinds of delusion that one could be said to believe (1) a delusion of **persecution** and (2) the **delusion** of reference. First, a **persecution delusion** is a "belief that others, often a vague "they" are out to get them" (Smith, M., and Segal, J., 2017, pp.4). A **persecution delusion** is a very common kind of delusion that is quite wide-spread among the young people all over the world. A **persecution delusion** really tricks one's own mind into believing that others are against them when this simply may not be the case. This of course is dangerous not only to the one that suffers this particular kind of delusion, but could of course potentially be harmful to others that they think they are out to harm them when it is just not the case. Another very common kind of delusion that sometimes interrelates and overlaps with a **persecution delusion** is the **delusion of reference** that could be said to incorporate "**ideas of reference**" that happen not to be true. The **delusion of reference (ideas of reference)** is "a neutral environmental event is believed to have special and personal meaning." (Smith, M., and Segal, J., 2017, pp. 4)   If let's say you interpret what is actually frivolous in meaning in how others behave to have special meaning, where you think that they are trying to send you message when it's not the case- this could be said to be the **delusion of reference.** This of course could have very negative consequences for themselves or others that we don't want or need. Delusion and hallucination is the most major symptoms in what actually puts one's mind "**out of reality**" to get that same person labeled a **schizophrenic."**

Chapter 14

Past And Present Treatment For Delusion

aturn

Prior to World War II if you were diagnosed as schizophrenic that you were then committed to a mental hospital for life much of the time. "For more than half of the century, most people diagnosed with serious schizophrenia were institutionalized in a public mental hospital." (Ronald Comer, 2007, pp.495)

After WWII many of the soldiers that served in WWII suffered post-traumatic stress from the war. The rise of outpatient counseling began to develop out- patient facilities then that began to grow rapidly, where they could get the medical help that they need for their sickness. The rest of the general population too got in on the new kind of out-patient medical treatment that was becoming more and more popular. Outpatient doctors and psychiatrists were now treating the general population at out-patient clinics from everything from depression right up thru schizophrenia. Outpatient treatment for those with mental illness proved very quickly quite successful. Even those that were psychotic with schizophrenia that ordinarily might be hospitalized for long periods of time were now allowed to stay in the free world-many of them not only taking care of themselves, but working jobs on their own, being productive citizens. According to Ronal Comer:

aturn

In the 1950's, clinicians developed two institutional approaches that finally brought some hope to patients who and lived in institutions for years: milieu therapy, based on humanistic principles and the token economy program based on behavioral principles. These approached particularly helped improve the personal care and self-image of patient's problem areas that had been worsened by institutionalization. The approaches were soon adapted by many institutions and are now standard features of institutional care.)

Another factor for why there was progress on behalf of the schizophrenic pertained directly to the findings of Klaus Conrad on Delusional thinking. During WWII Klaus Conrad was doing his life-time research on schizophrenia. He interviewed 108 soldiers from the German army that were in the early stages of schizophrenia. He discovered that in the case of many of these same soldiers that there was a special meaning or symbolic meaning coming alive to what they seen that led them to believe that others were trying to send them a message with it when it was just not the case. "The relatively new field of HR research in psychosis is exciting. It has the potential to shed light on the development of major psychotic disorders and to alter their course. It also aturn provides a rationale for service provision to those in need of help who could not previously access it and the possibility of changing trajectories for those with vulnerability to psychotic illnesses." With this research on the table it was now to realistically possible to believe that indeed delusion was rationally understandable and not rationally un-understandable as Jasper thought to be the case! This was of course a major breakthrough in how we understand delusion that has since led us to a greater success rate with those that have delusion to now rise above it. Simply if we can pin-point what got someone was thinking that caused them to jump to a false conclusion we are well on our way to ending delusion altogether and the dreaded schizophrenia in man. The people that research schizophrenia that followed Conrad by now almost all of them like Conrad take the position that delusion is rationally understandable in most cases. They share the optimism together that we are now getting more people to rise above delusion by better understanding why we jumped to a false conclusion and literally dwell in a bad fantasy about others. I too share in the optimism that the other researchers of today have that we can get people to rise above delusion.

aturn

Even though there was significant progress for those that have been labeled schizophrenic on a large scale basis nation-wide, people that were labeled schizophrenic might still need to go to the hospital for a few weeks so that they can overcome a present delusional episode that they are having. Still and all this of course represents significant progress on behalf of the schizophrenic that now can still avert being put in hospital all the time for the rest of their life.

In Recovery From Delusions, which was a study about those temporarily hospitalized for delusion, the patients being tested recovered from there delusional state within less than a month's time. It usually took about twenty days on the average for them to come back out of a delusional state with the help of anti-psychotic drugs and therapy at the hospital.

According to this same article there are three general phases in coming back out of delusion. "Based on these findings, we have defined three stages in the course of delusional thinking. Initially, in the delusional phase, the patient is totally involved in his delusions. This is followed by the double-awareness phase, where reality testing and trust coexist with the delusions. On recovery, a third, non-delusional phase occurs." (Sacks, M., H., Carpenter, W., T., Strauss, J.,

S., Bethesda, 1974, pg. 118) It is important to know though that there is no guarantee that they will not be plagued again by a new delusion, but for the time being when they show significant signs of recovery from delusion they are then allowed to stay in the free world once again. Now of course we want long-term recovery from delusion and not just short-term relief from it, but there is no absolute guarantee that the patient will not fall into delusion again.-especially without continued therapy of medicine and counseling.

Now wouldn't it be nice if we could all just learn to stop on a dime with delusional thinking, when we are entering one, so that we never really believe the potential delusion that is starting to overshadow us. This of course is why I composed the diagram that explains the nature of delusion in a very simple straightforward and to the point way so that we can see thru how we began to develop an overall irrational belief even though it may have a logic to it, but better evidence points to the contrary. We can all indeed with education on the nature of delusion and good attitude in general learn to rise above it, by learning not to trust or be guided by ludicrous fears and lack of trust for the future even when we had better sound reason to believe that we could and should just keep acting in good faith with others- not trusting what we shouldn't but trusting to the point that we should that things are going to work out fine……!

In summary of this chapter once upon a time most people found to have serious mental illness were put in mental hospitals for the rest of their life. By now there are outpatient clinics that even that even those with schizophrenia attend and get help to live as delusion free life as possible. The ideal situation would be that when someone is even entering a delusion they stop on a dime with irrational thinking- symbolic meaning coming alive to what other do does not then mean necessarily that other were trying to send you a message, and avert delusion altogether.

Chapter 15 Who Were And Now Are The Most Major Researchers On Schizophrenia And Delusion?

aturn

The two biggest named thinkers and researchers on the topic of schizophrenia and delusion is Karl Jasper who did his work at the beginning of the nineteenth century which is really the first accepted scholarly work on schizophrenia ad delusion, and then Klaus Conrad followed in the middle of the nineteenth century when he made a great discovery and/or innovation about delusioon.

Karl Jasper gets credited for inventing this concept-what a terrible and potentially dangerous disorder that creeps inside of people! A delusion of course is to believe something that is just not the truth, even after we have been given superior evidence to the contrary. This of course can be dangerous not only to the person that is having the delusion, but it can be dangerous and deadly to us all sometimes. According to Jasper those entering delusion are caught up in a state of confusion that he refers to as a delusional cloud. A delusional cloud is a cloud of confusion that has "subjective passion" towards believing that which is just not true. (The fact that one is believing something with "subjective passion" as opposed to just a fleeting thought that they are having let's say, convinces them sometimes beyond refutation from others that it is true even when it is not true. That means then that they cannot be easily talked out of believing what they think is the case, but is not the case.)   Also according to Jasper delusion is ultimately un-understandable. "In this section my object has been to introduce the primary experience as one of the true criterion of pathologically falsified judgement: and un-understandably as its trade…." This is important of course because if we can't find out what in the light of good sense what is causing them to believe what they do, and you can't talk them out of believing it then man we have a problem on our hands!

By the middle of the nineteenth century Klaus Conrad comes along as a viable researcher on the topic of schizophrenia- delusion in particular foremost. Like Jasper, Conrad believed that people entering delusion are brought into a delusional cloud of confusion. They could be said to believe what they do with subjective passion even though it's not true but cannot be easily talked out of believing this. But unlike Jasper, Conrad thinks that delusion can be rationally understood and that indeed one might be able to reach those with delusion to change them. "Borrowing from ancient Greek, the artificial term apophany describes this process of repetitively and aturn monotonously experiencing abnormal in the entire surrounding...." (when the delusional looks around he or she misreads the true meaning of the behavior of other.)

Klaus Conrad interviewed 108 soldiers that had the beginning symptoms of schizophrenia. What Conrad in effect realized was that these young soldiers experiencing delusion all were experiencing a special meaning that includes "symbolic meaning" coming alive to what they literally saw that made them think that a message was being sent to them by others when this was just not the case. He called it the Effer Aha experience. Klaus Conrad's research that confirmed that delusion is rationally understandable marks a major breakthrough in how we approach this disorder! This major change in how we now approach delusion represented much more hope for possible recovery. It helped make recovery inevitable for the schizophrenic as a result in many cases. To pinpoint how one begins to believe a falsehood about whatever even after they have been given superior evidence to the contrary helps the victim of delusion to now understand the obvious irrationality of their delusional thinking: if I as a potential victim of delusion can now get thru my head that just

aturn

because a symbolic meaning has come alive to me it does not then necessarily mean that someone else was trying to send us a message thereby, but of course the symbolism that we experience here could just be a coincidence. We can then in effect much more easily get the patient or victim of delusion to overcome it. What a fool believes he receives, so we had better be hip to how this delusion came about to curtail and end it. Again more self-awareness and education on what caused us to believe a lie can help us turnaround or rise above it. Since the time that Klaus Conrad did his studying on delusional thinking the overwhelming majority of those that followed him also took this same point of view that delusion is understandable. And "yes' this of course changed radically how we approach delusion that helped bring about a positive correlation between the idea that delusion is understandable and a higher success rate in getting the patient to rise above delusion. Whereas just a short time ago before their were outpatient clinics for schizophrenics along with the work of Conrad that delusion is understandable- people were hospitalized the rest of their life in many cases but now they were receiving treatment that was helping them rise above delusion and need only very temporary hospitalization most of the time, or none at all to get them aturn to see past delusion. Oh hallelujah! We have literally moved from darkness to light in terms of how we treat schizophrenia. There has been sheer joy, hope and optimism since the time of Conrad that we can now understand this disorder well enough to know how to overcome it.

Next, I cannot begin to recount in just a few pages all of the progress in schizophrenic research directly related Conrad's breakthrough that delusion is understandable, but of course it is significant. (We don't need to jump to false conclusions about the true meaning of other people's behavior, but find out the truth instead and rise above delusion accordingly.) So what are some of the outstanding post-Conrad researchers on schizophrenia doing to better bring about an awareness of this disorder? We have the research of today that includes the likes of Frith, Lyasker, Bucci, Startup, Ruiz, Melinda Smith, Jeanie Segal, Zou, Arthur. Wang, Hu just to name some that have all made significant contributions as far as I am concerned to help people to rise above delusion or mental illness in general.

aturn

First of all I want to Salute Melinda Smith and Jeanie Segal for their tireless efforts in helping **to educate all of us about the nature, potential causes and potential consequences of schizophrenia.** A tremendous article that by now has been updated that is presently referred to as schizophrenia, Symptoms, Signs, and Coping Tips by both of these same two people deserves the Presidential medal of honor for them. I know it has done so much good to "hip up" the masses about what this dreaded disorder is all about. This particular article that I just alluded to Schizophrenia Symptoms, Signs, and Coping Tips is clear, scrutible, and understandable for almost anyone that is willing to read it. It is out of sight in terms of how valuable a tool it is to educate the masses on a disorder that was thought to be un-understandable till Klaus Conrad shows up in the 1950's. Education itself on the nature of schizophrenia itself has been a useful tool in combating this terrible disorder! Unfortunately Jeannie Segal has passed away from cancer in 2017, but Melinda Smith as far as I know is still working hard in the field of psychology to help stop the spread of mental illness. I can say that this same particular article: Schizophrenia Symptoms, Signs, and Coping Tips by them inspired me to the point that it created a driving force in me that to keep learning

aturn

more of the conventional wisdom for this disorder till the time I wrote my masters on schizophrenia. I am proud to say that my master's not only met with approval, but I think it is a valuable help guide on better understanding schizophrenia. It elaborates beyond just how we define schizophrenia; and it causes; and it consequences, to also even understanding other related disorders to schizophrenia; to the history of the field of research in this field; to a serious discussion of how we should be able to overcome delusion. Let's keep caring about those who are mentally ill with schizophrenia and help them get past delusion instead of judge them!

Next, No less exciting news is that they are now educating the patients themselves on the nature of their disorder, so that they might more easily and quickly overcome it! I am excited about it because I know it is really helping the patient of delusion to rise above it and ditch schizophrenic symptoms for good! An interesting article that alludes to this latest trend in helping the recovery of those with delusion called Self- Management Education Interventions by Zou H., Zheng L., Nolan, M., Arthur, D., Wang H., Hu, L., 2013 proclaims: : " Finally, 13 studies with 1404 patients were included. Self-

aturn

management education were associated with a significant reduction of relapse events and re-hospitalizations. Patients who received self-management education were more likely to improve adherence to medication and symptoms compared to patients receiving other care. However, a benefit on psychosocial education intervention is a feasible and effective method for persons with schizophrenia and should be routinely offered to all persons with schizophrenia." In this study one of the categories for self-management to the recovering patient there is a category that was included that involves teaching the patient of schizophrenia more about the nature itself of this terrible disorder. This of course is extremely good news as this then makes it clear with self-management classes that include education on the nature itself of this disorder then makes a difference positively in reducing relapse in this disorder as a result of this training. Isn't that exciting news?! It is to me! Hallelujah!   Please keep these self-management classes that incorporates an understanding of schizophrenia itself rolling along for us!

Next, the work of Dorothy Ruiz, a formiable researcher on schizophrenia, I cannot say enough for! She proclaimed boldly that schizophrenia equals delusion....! In Epidemiology of Schizophrenia: Some Diagnostic And Sociocultural Considerations Ruiz says" Schizophrenia is an illusive illness. **The symptoms consist of delusions of persecution or reference not occurring in the context of severe depression; grandiose, religious, somatic or bizarre delusions, but not in a setting sf severe depression or mania; disorder thought and body control: and hallucinations, but not depressive in content and not symptomatic of alcohol addiction."** (pg 315 par.2) I can agree whole heartedly with Dorothy Ruiz in this statement to the point I want to shout it on the roof also! "Schizophrenia is delusion!" "Schizophrenia is delusion!" This is of big importance that Ruiz says just that because it is delusion that is the most major symptom of the five because which actually really takes one away from reality that is common to all of the rest of us. But if someone that has the symptoms of schizophrenia will rise above delusion they could be said to be almost always back to a normal state of mind even if they still have some problems with their nerves left. Ruiz for this reason wants to drive home the point that "yes indeed" delusion is the most major subtype of schizophrenia, so that we will pay special attention to it.

aturn

Second, Ruiz also highlights the fact that one can sometimes be false-diagnosed with schizophrenia when they in fact do not have it, or their symptoms are culturally related. Ruiz claims in her analysis about false diagnosis that those that are of black skin color often get labeled schizophrenic where this is a beefed up, and thus a not true analysis of their exact mental state "Collins, et al. in their retrospective study of a black inpatient population found a slightly lower rate of schizophrenia among black diagnosed by black diagnosticians supports the contention that racial and biases are factors contributing to misdiagnosis. The studies here suggest that black patients have a higher risk of being misdiagnosed than whites. Racial and cultural biases of the clinician are reported as factors contributing to the misdiagnosis." (pg. 3121 par. 1) Cultural differences sometimes that someone of the same color could more easily pick up on explains why a temporary fall away or potential conflict with others goes on when one is first meeting new friends. When it is the case that cultural differences stands between two people at least sometimes more understanding promoted between the two of them occurs a new friendship in many cases happens.

aturn

(There are yet other factors too for why someone might be false diagnosed a schizophrenic when in reality it is just not true. Someone that is deaf can be false diagnosed as schizophrenic because of the fact that he or she just can't hear as well as others then leads to potential misunderstanding between them and somebody else, wherein someone proclaims that this same person must be delusional instead of the deafness that it is. People that are deaf quite obviously can't hear as well and then sometime blurt out communication back that does not correspond back in meaning like it should. You can see too how it might be easier to become paranoid of suspicious of others, wherein communication falls apart with them all of the time..... Deafness is a private hell to those who have deafness!)

In Delusion of Reference A New Theoretical Model by Mike Starup, Sandra Bucci, And Robyn Langdon make an important update on this concept. That from now on when the particular delusion of reference that we are having happens to affirm the idea that someone is really attempting to communicate symbolically to you with their actions that this particular kind of delusion of reference should be more rightfully called the delusion of communication. I agree that this a good

aturn

distinction to make so we can better know what kind of delusion of reference we are talking about. I hope that for certain purpose it may still be appropriate to still refer to it as the broader and more encompassing word delusion of reference. Much thanks though for making this new useful distinction about how a delusion of reference can sometimes be seen as a delusion of communication.

Also In Delusion Of Reference: A New Theoretical Model by Mike Startup, Sandra Bucci, and Robyn Langdon- all three of these contemporary researchers have an extreme attachment to the work of Chris Frith in it. "According to Frith(1992), delusions of reference, together with persecutory delusions and third-person auditory verbal hallucinations (i.e.., voices conversing),result from a disorder of Theory of Mind (ToM). **ToM refers traditionally to the capacity to represent and to infer the casual mental states (e.g. The beliefs and intentions) of self and others in order to predict and explain behavior."** Theory of mind is the ability to attribute mental states — beliefs, intents, desires, emotions, knowledge, etc. — to oneself and to others. Theory of mind is necessary to understand that others have beliefs, desires, intentions, and perspectives that are different from one's own.[1] Theory of mind is crucial for

aturn

everyday human social interactions and is used when analyzing, judging, and inferring others' behaviors.[2] Deficits can occur in people with autism spectrum disorders, genetic-based eating disorders, schizophrenia, attention deficit hyperactivity disorder,[3] cocaine addiction,[4] and brain damage suffered from alcohol's neurotoxicity;[5] deficits associated with opiate addiction reverse after prolonged abstinence.[6] Theory of mind is distinct from philosophy of mind. (Wikepedia)

So then the Theory of the Mind pertains to how one interprets the behavior of one's own self or others behavior as well. As already stated, According to ToM in effect we are making value judgements about the mental states of one's self or others that is capable of telling us the beliefs, intents, desires, emotions, or knowledge of others in the plight of what they do. For example if you see kids playing outside the front of a corner bread store, and one of them keeps looking in the direction of the store you could assume, as leap and jump as this is, that he was making plans to rob the store soon just from seeing this. Or like for example if you were to see a supervisor standing with one hand on his hip, that does this every day, watching the crew under him on the assembly line you might infer that he is trying to show his desires and emotions related to the crew getting more quality parts out. Or like for example you seen someone in a shirt and tie walking around at the factory that needed rebuilding walking around with a just rolled up paper in his hand you could jump to the false conclusion also that he was also assessing how a construction company would soon be revamping the building even though you have heard of no plans for your business to go ahead with any construction soon. Or like for example if someone at work always walked around with a pencil above his ear at work that it mean't that he thought he was very brainy! All of the just given examples of where you may be inclined to believe that you can read the will of others can be considered ToM because you are focusing on the potential meaning of others behavior that goes beyond just what you can literally assess about the potential meaning in itself, and believing that you can really figure out the mental state of others!

    I would not be inclined to always jump to the conclusion though that because someone thinks that they can guess what is inside someone's head that means that what they believe is not true, but when it is improbable or dubious in light of all of the circumstances related to it, it is usually considered a possible delusion. Then a whole other separate issue is whether someone could be trying to send others a message with their particular behavior exhibited and probable mental state behind it or is this not the case? ToM if understood correctly does not necessarily imply a message being sent by others, but is focusing more directly on what this could reveal about the mental state itself of others. That is not to say that symbolic communication by others does not indeed go on though sometimes. The concept of ToM was created by British scientist Chris Frith who has spent many, many years studying the disorder of schizophrenia. This concept is widely used to reinforce the idea that we as people on this earth think that we have the ability to know the mental state one's self or others, which can be important to know. If we know can understand the mental states of others then we just might be able to know what others may be up to or why then they are up to it if and only when it is really an accurate mind-reading! Still Is this really possible though one might ask one's self?.

Next, I want to explain in more detail discuss Jasper's concept of the delusional cloud, and then show why it is inadequate to believe as it is not an entirely accurate guide or tool for us in understanding delusion: 1) First as it pertains to Jasper's delusional cloud- a cloud of confusion where what you are observing now comes alive in a new way that could be said to have subjective passion related to it. Second, it is beyond refutation or incorrigibility for this same person to be now talked out of what they are passionately beginning to understand and believe that is false. Third, it is not rationally understandable what this same person is now believing. Like Jasper, Conrad too believes in a delusional cloud that (1) has subjective passion to it and (2) it is also hard to correct this same person of what they are possibly beginning to believe, but for Conrad delusion can be rationally understood. That means that even if there is a cloud of confusion hanging over people with delusion, we may at least more easily sometimes reach the victim of delusion to change their mind about what they believe that is a falsehood. (For Conrad there is sometimes a symbolic meaning coming alive to what one witnessed in the environment that is sometimes understood by this same person as potentially symbolic communication from others or a message then from them. An internal dilemma may start in this person that involves literally asking one's self does the symbolic meaning coming alive to them really mean that someone was trying to send me a message or is the symbolic meaning that has come alive in this case

aturn

merely coincidental. Mature judgement is not easily swayed to believe that which should not be believed! And if someone is enlightened too they can see cause and effect much more quickly realize that they should not be believing that which is not fully rational for sure.)

    The overall complaint then with Jasper's delusional cloud is that one is stuck here at this juncture of a delusional cloud of confusion since Jasper believes that schizophrenia is not rational understandable. ! Quite obviously if we cannot get out of a totally confused state of mind that he claims goes on this step of the entrance of delusion then we of course have a much smaller chance for recovery!!!

    But then of course if delusion is indeed really rationally understandable like it is for Conrad then we can and should be able to rise above delusion with the right help! Counseling, with education on the nature of this disorder itself for the patient allowing the patient and doctor both to look at the social, environmental, and psychological conditions make all of the difference in the world for the better! This point of view is really working leaps and bounds of success! Oh hallelujah!

aturn

But now one very important remark of caution about over-optimism- is that even though with the right help in many cases one can rise above delusion, it still sometimes takes a little time for this to happen. And "yes" do remember that delusion has subjective passion to it where the victim of delusion is convinced in their own mind of that which is just not true; and without the right help can in many cases not be talked out of believing the falsehood! I at least hope we all have the right attitude toward those with mental illness! They are really in a confused state of mind and don't need a stick over their head or beat up for the proper remedy but instead treatment from a physician! Love our schizophrenics and route for them to get better, not hurt them!

Next, in an extremely insightful and useful scholarly journal article: Paul Lysaker, Jack Tsai, Kristin Hammond, & Louanne W. Davis called Patterns Of coping Preference Among Persons With Schizophrenia: Associations With Self- esteem, Hope, Symptoms and Function, we are told that of 133 hospitalized patients, they were placed into five different groups of people. Of the five different groups of people all five showed different tendencies of coping. In group 1) persons who

aturn

had a preference for both acting and considering ii) persons who had a preference for acting alone iii) persons who had a preference for considering and resigning iv) persons with preferences for ignoring v persons that had no clear preference for any coping style. They were compared with each other for assessments of hope, self-esteem, symptoms and social function. Of the five different groups it was the group that had the preferred coping style of both acting and considering that did the best all-around in terms of how well they managed their attitude

functioned with others the most satisfactorily. (Lsyaker, Tsia, Hammond, and Davis, pp.198)

So now to be considerate and resourceful in general more helps to get people to think better where they now work together better with others, and this survey confirms it. It is proof that among schizophrenics a positive attitude does play an important role in helping us to succeed in everyday life to get along with others better. No doubt too, we all could function better in life with a better attitude: one that encompasses both the willingness to be action

aturn

oriented when we should be and be considerate of all others to the point that we should be to help make us a winner!

Chapter 16

My Ideas On Rising Above Delusion:

 Now finally I would like to tell you about an innovation and tool of my own that help sheds light on the nature of delusion that I think we should all be aware of. I have composed a diagram that tells us in just four simple real steps of the actual thoughts of someone how they then enter into delusion from a non-delusional state of mind. In the first place one literally witnesses or hears something real that is usually in the same environment. Secondly, one experiences a symbolic meaning coming alive to what one literally saw or heard. In the third step one is wondering whether the symbolic meaning that has come alive to them in their thoughts is really a message in the form of symbolic communication being sent to them. In the fourth step one decides one way or the other whether the symbolic meaning that has come alive to them is really symbolic communication being

aturn

sent to them by others. The following is the diagram itself that I have composed that should help reveal how one could be said to enter delusion in "yes" just four simple steps of one's thought process:

Part I An Understanding Of My diagram Itself:

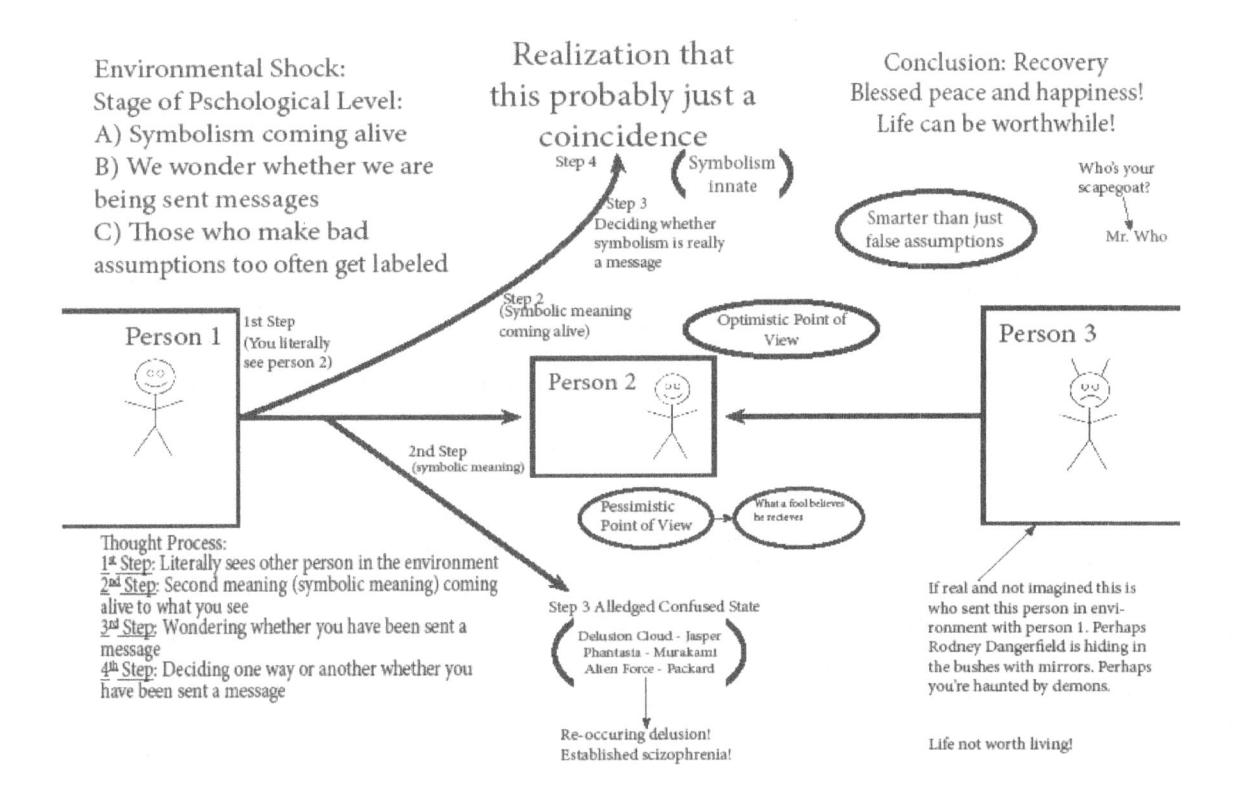

Environmental Shock:
Stage of Pschological Level:
A) Symbolism coming alive
B) We wonder whether we are being sent messages
C) Those who make bad assumptions too often get labeled

Realization that this probably just a coincidence
Step 4
Symbolism innate
Step 3
Deciding whether symbolism is really a message

Conclusion: Recovery
Blessed peace and happiness!
Life can be worthwhile!

Who's your scapegoat?
Smarter than just false assumptions
Mr. Who

Person 1
1st Step
(You literally see person 2)

Step 2
(Symbolic meaning coming alive)

Optimistic Point of View

Person 2

Person 3

2nd Step
(symbolic meaning)

Pessimistic Point of View

What a fool believes he recieves

Thought Process:
1st Step: Literally sees other person in the environment
2nd Step: Second meaning (symbolic meaning) coming alive to what you see
3rd Step: Wondering whether you have been sent a message
4th Step: Deciding one way or another whether you have been sent a message

Step 3 Alledged Confused State
Delusion Cloud - Jasper
Phantasia - Murakami
Alien Force - Packard

Re-occuring delusion!
Established scizophrenia!

If real and not imagined this is who sent this person in environment with person 1. Perhaps Rodney Dangerfield is hiding in the bushes with mirrors. Perhaps you're haunted by demons.

Life not worth living!

aturn

I believe first, that this diagram is a good educational tool that has much pragmatic value for getting people to see exactly how they became delusional. It gives a clear direct rational and objective approach to how one could be said to enter delusion. Using this diagram should help one to see in a very direct and pin-pointed way how one got off a fully rational course of thought and swept into believing that which is just not true about others or anything else in reality that one can be said to reflect on. Then second this should then in effect help you to rise above delusion. If it then helps us to not only to see exactly how we developed a false picture of reality, but then gets us also to realize how we might avert delusion by staying fully rational when deciding the truth in our dilemma.

aturn

Let me now give you three fictitious examples utilizing this diagram to illustrate it's obvious ability to help us better understand the entrance of delusion into someone:

Hypothetical Example #1 Delusion Of Reference And Delusion Of Persecution:

You have lived in St. Paul Minnesota your whole life. You are only twenty-two yrs. old, and hard worker. The last few weeks you have been experiencing something quite weird in terms of how you perceive the behavior of other right in front of you throughout the day and evening. It now looks to you like many of them that you see in everyday life including those in the traffic even are going out of their way to send you a message with their behavior. Instead of it just looking like they are just going about their own business it now looks like they are really going out of their way to make point of some kind with their behavior-like a hint or innuendo or message moreover to you. They actually might gesture with a hand on their hip or shaking their head mildly when they happen to be near you or even yawn at you or drive in your way in the traffic that makes you think that this is a negative personal comment to you as opposed to just a coincidence.

aturn

You no longer are well upstairs sometimes because you are frustrated with anger over others not seeming to want to leave you alone. You tell yourself that you are going to remain civil and that what you are experiencing is probably a coincidence and related to a stage of psychological development where at you age you are now noticing more potential meaning to the behavior others, but other behavior as of late really seems otherwise like it is a deliberate attempt to hurt your pride and cause you to just give up! You to one degree or another actually believing that others are going out of their way in everyday life to give you mental turmoil that you don't deserve as far as you are concerned!

Now if we are to use the diagram to put into perspective this delusion that this young man is apparently having that others are against him based on negative signs of behavior out of them right in front of him, but the whole thing is really just one big coincidence. In the first individual thought of his thought process he is scrutinizing the behavior of others. In the second step (and thought) of the thought process he is ascertaining that their behavior to him symbolizes a negative sign in their behavior. In the third step and (thought in itself)

aturn

of the thought process he is asking himself if it is the case that what to him symbolize behavior not to accept him is really a deliberate sign sent by others as opposed to just a coincidence. In the fourth step (and thought of his overall thought process on this issue he decides that others must indeed be going out their way with a message to him with just the mundane things that they do right in front of him every day. He has now entered delusion because he is believing that others are against him when it is not true and his mind only imagines that others were really trying to give him a hint with their behavior.

We should note that It is really from the second to the fourth and final individual step of the overall thought process that he has decided that the special meaning that is coming alive to him in the second step means for sure in the fourth step that others behavior around him was really a deliberate message being sent to him by others. It is also clear then too that in the third step and thought of the overall thought process, (where he now asks himself did someone indeed try to send me a message with their behavior or was it just coincidence?), where this same person to stay calm and rational enough in deciding whether or not he is being sent a message by others or not. (Even though it may be logical in one sense to believe that others sent him a message, the overall logic in deciding accurately this question still lacks enough serious rational evidence to believe that someone really went out of their way to send him a message.) Then finally it is then in the fourth step and thought in itself of the overall thought process while entering delusion that even though the victim of delusion still lacks crucial evidence to affirm that a real message is being sent to him he does so anyhow. Right then and there one actually has become fully delusional or now believing an absurd falsehood about the meaning of others behavior.

   So then obviously when we ask ourselves the question, were we being sent a message by others it is important to remember to stay fully rational and not rely on your emotion; fears, doubts, and suspicions just in themselves, but also use sound reason along with the facts that make it clear in most cases what to believe about others! What something may symbolize to us does not then necessarily mean that others sent us a message at all, but this takes good well now its human nature! It is really innate in many cases symbolic meaning that comes alive to us and does not then necessarily mean that anyone were sending us a message!

aturn

Learn not to jump to false conclusions just because there is a symbolic meaning to us that comes alive in what we see, hear, or just think about! This is sometimes considered delusion when we do this-honest!

Hypothetical Example #2 Hallucination:

Now in Los Vegas, Nevada there is usually quite a bit of business at the casinos in the middle of the fall. You are there to gamble just a few days before Halloween when you experienced the first hallucination that you had ever had in your entire life. You were waking up about 8:00 AM over at you hotel room when just as you opened your eyes you seen very clearly a goon like looking man that was crouched along the wall near the entrance/exit door smiling and coughing too and then laughing. You think, "well if this ain't a startling observation this hour of the morning when you didn't even happen to have a hangover" You took a deep breath, sat up in bed and rubbed your eyes and then after that when you were still looking intently in aturn the same direction this almost scary looking guy that was crouched by the door you notice is now gone. You jump out of bed and walk up to the door passing by this area where you seen this guy, but whatever it is that you seen was still vanished. You tell yourself that it must have been an optical illusion that you had and/ or just the tail end of a dream that projected out in front of you while you were still coming out of your sleep. No matter what I tell myself though I can't get over how real and vivid this apparent hallucination was. I had always thought prior to this experience that I just had that that hallucinations probably never even really happened to someone, but that it was just a lie that someone made up by them to because they need an excuse to pretend that they were sick....! You are right now shaken that anything that smacked of an hallucination then that really just happened to you, was again so real and life-like! Spooky!

    Now believe it or not the four step diagram that I have composed for delusion works for hallucinations too. Let me explain! If you remember with me that in the first step of the four step diagram that reveals how on might enter delusion it is in the first step that one literally sees, hears, or thinks what they are focusing on. Then in the second step we ascribe some kind of special meaning to it which then what you literally saw heard of thought about in the first step could now be said to symbolize something to you beyond just that. Then in the third step of course you ask yourself whether the symbolic meaning what has come alive in the second step means that someone was trying to send you a message pertaining to this symbolic meaning coming alive. And then once again in the fourth step you now believe or disbelieve that a message was being sent to you by others! Now in the case of this particular example where you experience an apparent hallucination where you see a guy crouched down by the door inside you hotel room that vanishes entirely w/o going out of the door, this should be seen as the first step of your thought process. The second step they could be trying to decide what this symbolized to them. In the third step one this same person could be asking what it they actually saw. And the fourth step they could decide whether what they saw was real or imagined. In the fourth step they decide perhaps whether they were being sent a message by another or this was all just an imagined hoax to one's head. Now even though a delusion is not an hallucination primarily, an hallucination has enough of the properties of a delusion that you could call it that for all practical

aturn

purposes, and my diagram can be used to explain what goes on in the thought process while we are deciding the true meaning of the hallucination too!

Hypothetical Example # 3 The Delusion of ESP About What Is Going On Behind Your Back:

You wonder much of the time whether you are still loved at the old karaoke bar that you used to sing at till a short time ago when you got sick with flu less than a month ago and had to quit going out singing because of your poor health. In the meantime as you recovered from the flu at home in the evening you were thinking about all of the details of what went on when you sang karaoke at Bernie's bar and grill! You now, as you are thinking about all of your experiences while you sang there- they were overall nice to you- but just before you got the flu or started to they seemed to all give you a cold shoulder of unfriendliness in there. You remember how the cook and the bar tender gave you a cold shoulder just before you got the flu. And they definitely had different friends than you. And when you were short a dollar for just a beer the bartender would not carry you for the dollar till the next time you sang there, but forced you to buy food and drink that you then put on your debit card with a ten dollar minimum purchase, if you use it which is what you had to do then. You feel especially hurt as you just keep dwelling on these memories that were good times that you had there. In your mind's eye you see some of them talking about you behind you're back in a negative way like they are not friends of you anymore. Anyways when you finally decide to go back after getting over the flu for sure they were now all nice to you whether this was just an act for business sake or they indeed really were your good friend? You think what is the difference? The end!

Now let's use the four step diagram on this particular delusion of ESP about what is going on behind your back to put into perspective how you began to believe that it is real. In the first step you're thoughts about what is going on behind you back as opposed to really seeing or hearing it right in front of you comes alive with an imagined picture of what it entails. In this fantasy you think that others are talking about you behind your back in a negative way and are against you hanging out at the bar/restaurant to sing. In the second step you are wondering whether whatever they really say behind your back constitutes a seriously bad attitude toward you. In the third step you are trying to decide whether or not that there is really a seriously negative attitude towards you that is building up behind your back or the whole thing is just

imagined. In the fourth step we decide that they indeed not only talk about you behind your back but that it really reflects ill-will towards you.

(This of course proves to be false and you were letting a negative imagination get away with you! We all occasionally day-dream about what goes on behind our back but we do not all then jump to the false conclusions that necessarily others are against us because of what we see in our imagination about what is probably going on behind our back.)

Comparing Symbolic Interactionism To The Delusion Of Reference:

Let's first begin with a definition of both symbolic interactionism and the delusion of reference and then compare and contrast in more detail the differences and similarities of both of them.

In the case of symbolic interactionism if you remember with me tells us that it is in "the actual interaction with others" in everyday life that is a big determining factor for how much we believe in others. It tells us precisely that it is by interacting with others in everyday life that includes all of the signs of communication including a smile or a handshake from them or even how they dress or their presence in itself that leaves us with a potentially lasting impression about how we then perceive others.

This is somewhat different of course than from what the definition of the delusion of reference means which is that when one looks around in the same environment that they are in they see for instance something in the behavior of others or in the makeup of the environment itself that causes them to then believe a falsehood about others, inspite of the fact that they have been presented with better rational evidence to the contrary.

Next what are the similarities between these two concepts? First, what these two concepts could be said to have in common with each other, is that with both symbolic interactionism and the concept of the delusion of reference either one they both could be said to include

aturn

literal facet- to- face- interactions with others- or in the case of the delusion of reference at the very least passive observation of others or other objects in the same environment that you are in. Second, they both could be said to focus not just on what the literal meaning in itself all by itself could be said to entail, but what also could that same behavior could be said to imply to you! Third in the case of both they literally one ask one's self in their thought process what is s the potentially meaning to the behavior of others behavior be said to then mean for them. Fourth in the case of symbolic interactionism or the delusion of reference either one the thought process of the mind finally arrives at a particular conclusion about what this then tells them about the other guy.

So then too what are the differences between the process of symbolic interactionism and the delusion of reference? The chief difference here is that when we experience a delusion of reference that we necessarily universally went thru the process of symbolic interactionism, but on the other hand when we go thru the process of symbolic interactionism in itself it does not then necessarily mean that we will also then be said to experience a delusion of reference or then we possess a false belief about others even though we were presented with superior evidence to the contrary.

Next, it is also interesting to note that if you were to attempt to plot in a diagram the on-going thought process itself of either symbolic interactionism or the delusion of reference they both fit nicely into my four step diagram to explain how this came about. First in the case of the process of symbolic interactionism, we first literally seen whatever we did in the behavior of others. Then second what special meaning does this literal behavior then imply to a four step progression for both oechanics or make up of symbolic interaction and the delusion of reference there is a striking similarity between them. If we are to just for the fun of it put the concept of symbolic interactionism into the four step model for delusion: In the first step let's say we saw someone coming the other way in a tweed suit extending their hand to shake ours. In the second step it stands out to you that it was a very firm handshake that they gave you. In the third step you are wondering whether they are a sincere negotiator or not based partially on the handshake that you just received from him. In the fourth step you tell yourself that the fact that he gave you a hearty

aturn

handshake in step two that this just might make you that much more of a believer in how sincere you perceive they are in really negotiating. Now using a hypothetical example of a delusion of reference put into perspective in the four step diagram let's say that you saw in the first step an old friend from California that was wearing a red shirt and white nylon pants. In the second step the fact that he is wearing a red shirt and white pants to you symbolizes possible support for the Southern California Trojans football team. (This is a special symbolic meaning coming alive to you.) In the third step you ask yourself the question did your friend wear red and white today to show support for the SC Trojans football team? In the fourth step you ask you decide that it is not likely true that this is why he wore this because he comes from Northern California and not Southern California.

Now even though it has little or no practical value to put the concept of symbolic interactionism into this four step diagram to solve any practical problem that I am aware of, but if you put both of these in perspective by using the four step model that is used in the diagram for delusion, it does let you see how in the third and fourth steps of it they follow the same pattern of logic used. In symbolic interactionism

aturn

if you remember with me we actually ask ourselves a question: is the special meaning that came alive to what we seen or heard in the second step when using this diagram mean that it has a real connection to what you now believe in the fourth step. There is then an important similarity between the mechanics of understanding delusion in itself and the mechanics of symbolic interactionism in itself. They both ask the question in the third step does the special meaning of what stands out to them in the second step imply that a message was being sent to them in the form of symbolic communication, which in the fourth step they answer this question affirmative or negative to

    Now as it pertains to delusion do you know anyone that really wants to be perceived like a klutz or a dummy that is not an efficient competent person for every matter in life? Don't we all want to be perceived as a winner and not some kind of moron? Well in the case of delusion it happens to be the case that quite obviously delusion can color your understanding of reality in a way that may make you look aturn like some kind out of touch idiot that must not comprehend reality very well let alone how to deal with life's problems the most effectively. And let's face it we all want to be perceived as smart people in like that we really do know what is going on and how to deal with every issue along the way. No one really wants to be perceived as someone that has delusion! We want to be a shiny and resilient competent knower that is walking tall! If you remember with me first the stories of "cat in the hat" by Dr. Zuess- the cat with the high hat who was much of a loner always made a mess of everything that he did- at least on the surface. He is a colorful and humorous character, but after you get tired of his antics that cause trouble get old you get tired of feeling sorry for his mistakes and say to yourself, "he sure is an idiot! How could anybody goof so many things up?" He just plain really begins to get on your nerves in a negative way! At least that is my perception of him…! It is obvious to me that the "cat in the hat" or then this loveable but half idiotic guy could possibly be neurotic in that he tries to accomplish things all by himself without getting any help from anyone else. Also he just might be said to be delusional too but we do not know this for sure unless we know his thoughts! He for sure is a space head to the maximum though! Why does he go on all

aturn

by himself without asking others for advice on how to solve many of the practical problems that he has —at least that?

Then on the other hand the sitcom story of the Fonz or then Henry Winkler. The Fonz is a young person that is either in his late teens or early twenties that rides a motorcycle and wears a t-shirt and leather jacket. He is full of fun, wit and humor. All of the young people cast in the show including Ronnie Howard like him and look up to him. They are cast as bright young men that just might be the future of America. The Fonz is a folk hero of a sort that always has a plan for the situations that arise in everyday life for one or another of them on this show. For a young person he seems less naive than others of them and seems to have little delusion at such a young age. He is really a cool guy that can walk on the water so to speak in everyday circumstances for just a young person! The Fonz is a natural problem solver; he always has a plan up his sleeve to solve problems and make things work right again! After all he is the Fonz himself, and this show was always a scream of fun in my opinion!

Well now if we are to then compare the characters of "cat in the Hat" and the Fonz, would you say like most people, hooray for the

aturn

Fonz in his ability to solve the problems arise in the everyday situations that he finds himself in, and at best deep down inside continue to pity or feel sorry for the "cat in the hat" for all his mistakes. And his mistakes are not funny even if this is how we are supposed to perceive him. What's funny about someone that is so ignorant that they are continually confused about how to make it thru the day without messing up everything! Although cat in the hat does not always appear to be paranoid, but more than not confident in his ability- at least starting out, he really begins to have much fear and anxiety as he plunders on all by himself making one mistake after the next. He is a confused nowhere man! He has no friends that we know of and never gives anybody else the time of day to say hi that I was ever made aware of or bother to ask a question on how to solve a problem. The Fonz on the other hand has plenty of friends because he shows himself friendly to others. Even the Fonz with all his wit and humor still needs a friend to comfort or guide him on a bad day too though. The Fonz also obviously has not too bad an understanding of what makes others ticks for just a young person. Overall The Fonz shows he can work together with others effectively, while the cat in the hat is a loner on his own even when he obviously could use help from others!

   So again now do we want to be clear headed and on the ball like "Fonz walking on the circumstances in life. or do we want to be like 'cat in the hat falling thru the ice every day in a paranoid, and confused state of mind. Well we want to be like the Fonz or course, perhaps not with the exact same personality or outlook on life, but in that we stay on top of things with a good attitude towards others that the Fonz apparently has. We'd rather be a hammer then a nail! We'd rather stand tall in the sunlight of life then be lost down a false trail of thought!

   That's why when it comes to delusion in itself or a false understanding of others and reality, when there is superior evidence to believe otherwise that if we know to consistently be rational in how we decide truth instead of act out of unwarranted fears then we would rise above delusion and see eye to eye with reality! (In this case the cat in the hat needed to interact with others when he should for advice to get him to rise above his fears.) I at least hope that the truth about delusion that my diagram itself uncovers will help you to

aturn

rise above it from now on! A complete overall education and understanding on the nature of schizophrenia itself can be vitally important. This is discussed in the next chapter, and then finally in the last chapter I challenge the young people- or all of us for that matter to acquire and maintain a positive attitude where we cannot only rise above delusion but stand on top of our everyday problems like we should be able to!

   In summary of this chapter my diagram that I composed it can be used as a tool to teach others with to better understand how not to be irrational and jump to false conclusions about others in everyday life. We must learn patience and tolerance in everyday life. We too must learn not to be irrational when we have ill-founded suspicion, but trust what we should and do not trust what we should not. Symbolic meaning coming alive that gets us to believe others are sending us a message when it simply not the case we don't want to adhere to, but rise learn to rise above a potential delusion altogether right from the start!

aturn

Part II Putting The Behavior Of Others Into Perspective: The who, what, when, where, why, and how of what others do

An ingenius way of putting into proper perspective an understanding of the most likely meaning of the behavior of others is to first ask ourselves what is the: who, what, where, when, why and how of why others did what they did in regards to you.

First as it pertains to understanding the meaning of others behavior we should ask ourselves "what it is that others actually did right in front of us. For example as it pertains to understanding the true meaning of the behavior of others we should first ask ourselves who did what this is that is the issue. Second we should ask ourselves what literally others may have been doing right in front of you that is part of the issue in question. Third let's ask ourselves when whatever occurred that stand out to you happened. Fourth we should ask ourselves where it happened also. And Fifth we should ask ourselves why or what then was the motive behind those that perpetrated whatever happened. And sixth how did they go about doing what they literally did in relationship to what you just experienced. All of

aturn

these questions are relevant and important that we answer to put into perspective properly what and why especially it occurred to you.

Now let's take a very simple example of a delusion illustrating how important that it really is to put it in proper perspective using the who, what, w here, when, why, and how of what went down in this incident that explains a lot of why it occurred that we should be aware of.

George Seibert was someone that everybody liked at work or wherever else he might find himself including among family or friends either one. For just a relatively short time period in his life from 22 to 24 he experience what he thought be uncalled for games from others in everyday life. Instead of just seeing literally what others were doing and then understanding the meaning of it in that way he now began to experience a second meaning coming alive to this same behavior being scrutinized- namely like what could this this behavior be said to really imply in the form of a hint, innuendo, insinuation or pun that they were really trying to send him a message. One day in fact George Seibert had an experience with his nerves or run away imagination that he almost got put into the hospital. In the early morning hour at work when he just got there he had just been thinking about female

aturn

that he was head over heels in love with that he thought he probably would never see again but wasn't altogether sure of that. to make a long story short that when he got to work on this same particular day that he first noticed a guy walking down the aisle that you knew that you know looks like the same guy that stole your X girlfriend. You know for sure that he is not the same guy that stole Rebecca from you, but you can't help but have the thought that when he walked by you right after you had just had thoughts about this particular female that broke your heart. It was as though his very presence in front of you was a staged affair where you think that he was trying to rub it in that Rebecca is now with someone else that look just about like him. Look you and this other guy have never been friends and you think just to be contrary he could deliberately be trying to hurt your feelings with his very presence. You are for a short time despising this same guy that looked like the guy that stole Rebecca from you, but not for long as you then tell yourself that the entire affair that you just experienced was nothing more than a coincidence and you have no business resenting this guy at work that should be your friend by now.

aturn

Now let's ask ourselves what is the: who, what, where, when, why, and how of this negative experience that you just had? First it is indeed another guy that you work with that seemed to you to be staging a game to rub it in that a guy that was not him but looked like him stole your Rebecca away from you. He indeed really worked with you every day during the week here. Second what he did was just walk by you on this same morning when you happened to be thinking of Rebecca. Third, when it happened was when you got to work early on this same morning. Fourth, where this incident occurred where you noticed this guy walking by was the main aisle. Fifth, why it is that he walked by in actuality must have really been just a coincidence or you know that your commonsense otherwise is waning. Sixth, how he did show up in your sight is by walking down the main aisle right when you were standing across the way from it. It is simply not to be believed that this was something being staged to you in the environment by him, but just a coincidence.

Now you can see with this brief illustration that I just gave how knowing the who, what, when, where, why, and how of the situation helps to shed intelligent light on what you should really know about aturn the experience that you just had in the scenario just given! Know this and it may keep you from misconstruing the truth about why others did what they did, and overall of course helps give you a more accurate picture of what went on that you are presently scrutinizing.

Chapter 17 Education on Delusion

I insist first of all that everyone should have a basic understanding of what schizophrenia really entails. Knowing the five symptoms of this disorder and the fact that one needs to exhibit two or more of these symptoms over a sixty day period of time to establish that one is psychotic and schizophrenic is important for us to know. This is really the legitimate way for deciding what schizophrenia entails, which is almost always delusion as the biggest player or symptom in this disorder. Delusion is the main sub-type of this disorder of schizophrenia.

aturn

Then second too we should all possess a detailed picture and understanding of the entrance of delusion itself like revealed in the diagram that I composed that explains that delusion enters one's mind in just four general steps of the thought process. Look we are all candidates for delusional thinking if we are not fully rational in how we jump to the conclusions that we make about the motive and intent of others behavior. We should all be aware of how we might be venerable to believing that which is not really fully rational if we have an un-natural kind of trust problem in others. We as smart human beings cannot necessarily trust any and everything others do, but there is an unspoken common sense kind of criteria that we should know about how not to act on ludicrous, unsubstantiated fears, but instead stay fully rational in our judgement of anything that others do, as opposed to let uncalled for fear or jumping the gun to false conclusions.

Without giving you a direct fact to support this claim I am going to say that delusion must be more widespread among our young people than what you might realize. Just because someone has not been labeled a schizophrenic according to the state does not mean that

aturn

they do not suffer delusion, not to mention other related disorders like obsessive compulsive, manic depressive or social anxiety and accompanying panic attacks perhaps. Just for one I know that there are a lot more young people with bad nerves than get labeled schizophrenic, but nonetheless many other people at least sometimes suffer mental disorders that are not considered serious enough to label schizophrenic. First, I base this on the fact that a lot more young people see psychiatric care than actually get technically labeled a schizophrenic. Those people that admit that they suffer social anxiety and obsessive compulsive behavior sometimes overlaps with delusion too. Second, I have observed for myself the conduct of young people in everyday life and they in many cases have secret fears that others are against them or they just can't do it with making the grade with work or education. They may even seem fearful that others are deliberately going out of their way in everyday life to tease them with the deliberate intentions of ill-will and rejection to them when it is not the case. They may really need coached that they can do it- to become a winner and an achiever like they are capable of being without delusion! Education on the nature of schizophrenia itself is a good place to start. If one can simply beat the symptoms of delusion aturn by rising above it then they may avoid the label schizophrenic being placed on them altogether!

For those that have already been labeled a schizophrenic there is hope too thru education on the nature of this disorder that is helping the patient to overcome it! Informing those that are patients for the treatment of schizophrenia In Self- Management Education Interventions by Zou H., Zheng L., Nolan, M., Arthur, D., Wang H., Hu, L., 2013. It has been demonstrated consistently that personal education for the patient on the nature of their particular disorder, in more detail has led to a significant reduction of relapse events and the need for re-hospitalization occurrence for delusional thinking. Isn't that exciting news?! It is to me! This is even more proof too that people then in general are rising above delusion more directly related to more personal education on the nature of their disorder! Beating delusion is the name of the game for all of us!

Mass literacy and education in general on the true nature of schizophrenia will help enhance all of our ability to rise above this terrible disorder! It is a great day coming because of the intervention of education as a tool to get people to rise above delusional thinking.

(We need also to feel loved by others, but delusion of course inhibits this. But let's not succumb to delusion, but rise above it, developing healthy interactions with others! "Carry on love is coming to us all!" (Crosby, Stills, Nash and Young))

Chapter 18

Attitude

And when they say that a good attitude is everything they are of course telling the truth. No one, absolutely no one wins like they should or is happy consistently, unless they have a good attitude! A good attitude of course is made up of an attitude that says I may not do everybody's work but I will contribute with my efforts like I should and that I will stay positive in how I treat others.- you know the golden Rule- Do unto others as you would have them do unto you- you know

aturn

treat others with love and fairness being no respecter of person but loving all with agape love.

    So then it is **work and love** after all like Jesus Christ talked about that is fundamentally important. **We first should examine the fiery whip of Matthew chapter 25** where it says that we should of course use our God-given abilities or we will be abased in the long-run. Mathew 25 verses 14 thru 30 says: "The kingdom of heaven is as a man travelling into a far country, who called his own servants and delivered unto them his goods. And unto one he gave five talents, and unto another two, and to another one to every man according to his several ability; and straightway took his journey. Then he that had received the five talents went and traded with the same, and made them other five talents. Ad likewise he that had received two, he also gained other two. But he that had received one talent went and digged in the earth, and his lord's money. After a long time the lord of those servants cometh, and reckoneth with them. And he that had received five talents cam and brought other five talents: behold I have gained beside five talents more. HI lord said unto him, well done thou good and faithful servant: thou hast been faithful over a few things, I

aturn

will make thee ruler over many things: enter thou into the joy of the Lord. He that had received two talents came and said, lord thou delivered me two talents: behold, I have gained two other talents beside them. His lord said unto him, well done, good and faithful servant; thou hast been faithful over a few things, I will make thee a ruler over many things: enter thou into the joy of the Lord. Then he which had received one talent came and said, Lord, I know that thou art an hard man, reaping where thou hast not strawed: And I was afraid and went and hid thy talent in the earth; Lo there thou hast that is thine. His Lord answered and said unto him; Thou wicked and slothful servant, thou knows that I reap where I sowed not, and gather where I have not strawed. Thou oughtest therefore to have put my money to the exchangers, and then at my coming I should have received mine own with usery. Take therefore the talent from him, and give it to which hath ten talents. For unto every one that hat shall be given, and he shall have abundance; but from him that hath not shall be taken away, even that which he hath. And cast ye the unprofitable servant into darkness; there shall be weeping and gnashing of teeth." Second, Matthew chapter 5 verse 3 thru 16 gives the "sermon on the mount" or better known as the "Be-attitudes."

aturn

This of course focuses directly on what constitutes a good attitude of love towards others in everyday life: "Blessed are the poor in spirit for theirs is the kingdom of heaven. Blessed are they that mourn" for they shall be comforted. Blessed are the meek: for they shall inherit the earth. Blessed are they which do hunger and thirst after righteousness: for they shall be filled. Blessed are the merciful; for they shall obtain mercy. Blessed are the pure in heart: for they shall see God. Blessed are the peacemakers; for they shall be called the children of God. Blessed are they which are persecuted for righteousness' sake: for theirs is the kingdom of heaven. Blessed are they when men shall revile you, and persecute you, and say all manner of evil against you falsely, for my sake. Rejoice and be exceedingly glad: for great is your reward in heave: for so persecuted they the prophets which were before you. Ye are the salt of the earth: but if the salt has lost its savour, where- with shall it be salted? It is thenceforth good for nothing, but to be cast out, and to be trodden under foot of men. Ye are the light of the world, A city that is set on an hill cannot be hid. Neither do men put a light a candle, and put it under a bushel, but on a candlestick; and it giveth light unto all that

aturn

are in the house. Let you light so shine before men, that they may see your good works, and glorify your Father which is in heaven."

In a study being done on those in recovery from delusion that I have already alluded to in chapter 8- Who Were And Now are The Most Major Researchers on Schizophrenia and Delusion called Patterns Of Coping Preference Among People With Schizophrenia. In this study by Paul Lsyasker, Jack Tsai, Kristin Hammod & Louanne w. Davis those recovering delusional thinking were put into four different groups of people. In one of the four groups all of them in the group were trying to **be both resourceful and communicatable** in how they would treat others. Those that were **resourceful and communicatable both** to others in everyday life showed signs of recovering much faster than those in the other three groups of people. Hallelujah these people recovered faster than if they had not showed this kind of a positive attitude towards others! This should be thought of as an important work that makes it clear- and not too leading, that even the mental illness of schizophrenia and delusion can be overcome if we are to show a good attitude towards others!

aturn

And did you ever meet anyone that did not have good attitude towards others that they succeeded for long? What is hate? What is the passion of ill-will like the joy love and comfort that comes inside from showing love?! If one were to stand back and examine ourselves and decide that we want to make a pact with the creator of the universe to work for good and not hurt others but to love others even with the love of God inside of us then we can succeed. And even if we don't claim to believe in God or Jesus, but do show a good attitude towards others than this should at least help! I don't know, it's just that I am a Christian and I know what worked for me like the supernatural aspects of believing in God that also gives me confidence. That not only I can walk on the water in everyday life and overcome, but that with a Big love inside of me and now even have hope of eternal life with Christ. But for sure a good attitude is something to be revered no matter who you are.

How many mountains in everyday life can we move if we do not show that we are resourceful and Yes that we love others as well with what we choose to do? To have a good attitude brings boldness and confidence in how we deal with others that helps us overcome

aturn

adversity! Faith is based on confidence! The world is as we are, let's treat others with love!

I read a story of motivation by Jesus Christ in the Bible, Mark 11:23 tells us: "For verily I say unto you, that whosoever shall say unto this mountain, Be thou removed, and be thou cast into the sea; and shall not doubt in his heart, but shall believe that those things which he saith shall come to pass; he shall have whatsoever he saith." We have faith which can come for the confidence boost that acting on Matthew chapter 25 (the story of the tem talents) and acting on Matthew 5 (the beatitudes) brings inside of us! Love conquers all!

I also read another beautiful story of motivation by Norman Vincent Peale called the Power Of Positive thinking. This tells us that we must stay positive in our outlook on life if we want to be a winner. A work ethic, self-examination, self- confidence, love, and prayer- all fit into his philosophy for successful living! Particular quotes from Peale that epitomizes this personal philosophy for living too: (1) In a publication called Goalcast, Peale is quoted as saying, "believe in yourself. Have faith in your abilities! Without a humble, but reasonable confidence in your own powers you cannot be successful or happy." (2) In the aturn publication Brainy Quote, Peale is quoted as saying, "Action is a greater restorer and builder of confidence. Inaction is not only the result, but the cause of fear. Perhaps the action you will take will be successful; perhaps different action or adjustments will have to follow, but any action is better than no action at all! " (3) In another quote from Brainy Quote, Peale says also, "One of the greatest moments in anybody's developing experience is when he no longer tries to hide from himself but determines to get acquainted with himself as he really is." (4) Yet also from Norman Vincent Peale in (AZ Quotes) on love says, "When you are wholeheartedly adopt a "with all your heart' attitude and go all out with the positive principle, you can do incredible things." (5) Yet one more saying from Peale- this one about the need for prayer in (Awaken The Greatness says, "Always start the day with prayer. It is the greatest of mental conditioners."

The Salvation of a good attitude is free and we can incorporate it! We can live in good conscience! Forget the hate, loving and digging each other is where it's at- routing for the best in others and the best in man and being a big brother and friend to all. Imagine little old me who was shy and almost a loser now with purpose and friends and

aturn

good times too. And just maybe I'll win my dream to sing China Grove with the Doobie Brothers and the Long Run with the Eagles but whether that happens or not I am glad that I have a good conscience and can accept myself, and that I am now bold enough to show love to all and for goodness sake will to make the positive difference of progress for the entire family of man! I want to help others overcome delusion! This has been a true dream of mine! Don't you think that we have all been there with depression, fear, doubt, paranoia, suspicion unto delusion or a false belief? We can do it though, when we show a good attitude- we can overcome and be a shiny happy person that we would idealize being! A good attitude makes delusion vanish! If we are smart we will realize that growing a heart for other- including giving it our best shot with constructive and creative endeavors, and yes treating each other with love and kindness like we should is essential. In Ephesians 4:32 it says, "Be ye kind one toward another tender-hearted, merciful, and forgiving one another even as Christ hath loved and forgiven us" Amen? Amen! Be blessed by this reading out of the Bible and Peale's inspiring positive thoughts. Remember to be a friend to others when its possible. And remember that what you do will come back to you….!

aturn

God bless you -Move "mountains of difficulty", with a Good Attitude towards all consistently! Make an attitude adjustment right now for the better if we need to! Step back, examine yourself knowing that self-acceptance is important and choose being Love, Help, and the way up!

If we are good like we should be there is nothing to fear, but fear itself, you are on your way with a good attitude inside that we show to others every day! With a Big Love inside we can overcome in everyday life! Don't give up loving others even in the face of adversity and you will come out on top!

A Final Thought: I thank all of my professors at Indiana University in South Bend, IN for a great education! This book reflects "The Power Of An I.U.S.B. Education" and also showing the initiative on my part to get out of bed at 4:30 A.M. for two yrs. to compose this book! Special thanks to all of my professors in graduate school including Dr. Joe Chaney, Dr. Betsy Lucal, Professor Julie Feighery, And Dr. Patrick Hubbard who personally guided my masters- all of these people taught, inspired and motivated me to keep on going till I won

aturn

my Master's thesis in 2018! I leave you with the lyrics of my favorite Kenny Loggin's song, Heart Of Light:

I like the love

And I like the peaceful

I wish everyone I know could

Stand in the heartlight

I hold the hand

I walk with the teacher

We welcome in the mornin'

Singing together

Can you feel the love that's in my heart?

Can you see the flame we got to start?

Burnin' like a beacon in the night

O welcome to heartlight

Oh oooh heart of light

Oh oooh heart of light

Oh oooh heart of light

aturn

Oh oooh heart of light

Oh oooh heart of light

Oh oooh heart of light

Oh oooh heart of light

Oh welcome to heartlight

I like the rain

'Cause I like your thunder

I know we've learned to live together

Here in the heartlight

Stand in the dark

Oh, oh and I'll light a candle

And then we'll dance it in the moonlight

Until the sunrise

Can you feel the love that's in my heart?

Can't you see the flame we've got to start?

Burnin' like a beacon in the night

aturn

O welcome to heartlight

Can you feel the love that's in my heart?

Can't you see the flame we've got to start?

Burnin' like a beacon in the night

O welcome to heartlight

Oh oooh heart of light

Oh oooh heart of light

Oh oooh heart of light

Oh oooh heart of light

Oh oooh heart of light

Oh oooh heart of light

Oh oooh heart of light

Oh oooh heart of light

Oh oooh heart of light

Oh oooh heart of light

aturn

Oh welcome to heartlight

Paul N. Johnson

Bibliography:

1. Action Oriented, Overview Google

2. American Psychiatric Association (2013) Diagnostic Statistical Manual, American Psychiatric Publishing, 5th Ed. Vol 7 Pg. 104

3. Approved Course Driving a motor vehicle is a privilidge and not a guaranteed right

4. Attribution- Oxford Dictionary

5. Bazaaar Delusion Web MD

6. Bengali, H., Daley, M.C. (2014) FRBSF Economic Letter, Is It Still Worth Going To College?

7. Bill Of Rights ACLU

8. Blumer Symbolic Interactionism

9. Cars Who Can It Be Now

10. Cargiulo, Thomas Understanding The Health Impact Of Alcohol Dependence (2007) American Society Of Health-System Pharmacists, Inc. DOI 10.2146/ajhp060647

11. Cocker Joe Lord Lift Us up Where We Belong

12. Cohn, James, Walkin' In Memphis

13. Comer, RJ (2007) Abnormal Psychology ninth Ed., New York: Worth Publishers pp. 495 Confabulation. (.nd) The Free Dictionary retrieved from Medical Dictionary. the free dictionary.com/confabulation

14. Confabulation- Healthline

15. Costa Raquel, Bastos Tania, Probst Michael, Seabra, Andreazo Vihena, Esticalela & Corredeira, Rui Autonomous Motivation And Quality Of Life as predictors Of Physical Activity In Patients With Schizophrenia International Journal Of Psychiatry In Clinical Practice. 22.3. 184-190 Doi10.1080/ 13651501.2018.1435821

16. Clauson, W., Galloway, S.A., Baerentzen, M.B., Britigen, F., (2016) Mental Health Journal

17. Climb Professional Development 7 Benefits Of effective Communication Portland community College

aturn

18. Crosby, Stills, Nash, & Young,

19. Dauwan, Bgeman, Heringa & Summer2016! Gacymski &Faulkner, 2010

20. Does Schizophrenia run in families? Quest Bright Treatment centerr

21. Drivers Ed. Driving a motor vehicle is a priviledge and not a guaranteed right!

22. Elmer Jamie Symptoms Of An Identity Crisis

23. Emerson, R. W., Nature, Penguin Books

24. Erotomania- Good Therapy

25. Falon, L. F. (2013), Schizophrenia. In Gale (Ed.) The Gale Encyclopedia Of Nursing And Allied Health, schizophrenia PP. 2

26. Fogerty, J., Lookin' Out My Backdoor

27. Genetics (2005) NHS

28. Goffman, E. (1959), The Presentation Of The Self In Everyday life New York, Anchor Books

29. Hall, Darrel, Oats John Private Eyes Their Watching You

30. In Structural abnormalities in the frontal system in schizophrenia: a magnetic resonances imaging study Jama Network

31. Hegel, G. W. "The Real Is the Rational"

32. Jackson, Michael- "One bad apple don't spoil the whole bunch girl"

33. Jackson Michael I Always Feel Like somebody's watching me

34. John Elton "Border Song"

35. Johnson, P.J. (2008) (My diagram on delusion)

36. Johnson, P.J. (2008) Schizophrenia Or Growing Pains

37. King, Carol Only Love Is A Reason

38. King Harvest Dancing in the Moonlight

39. Lennon, John Mind Games

40. Literary Devices

41. Little William Introduction To Sociology 2nd Edition

42. Little Feat, Sailin' shoes

43. Locke J. Google

44. Loes, Harry Dixon This Little Light Of Mine

45. Loggins, K. Google

aturn

46. Lysaker P.,Tsai, I, Davis, H&L., Patterns Of Coping Preference among persons With Schizophrenia Associations With Self-Esteem, Hope, Symptoms and Function, Journal Of Behavioral Consultation And Therapy, 5, (2), PP.198

47. Margolis, Russel Delusion and Deafness

48. Mayo Clinic Overview (Mood Swings)

49. Mayo Clinic PTSD

50. Men at Work Who Can It Be Now

51. MIshara, A.L., (2010), Klaus Conrad (1905-1961): Delusion, Mood, Psychosis, And Beginning

52. Mood Congruent Delusion- Wikipedia

53. Mood Neutral delusion-   Wikipedia

54. Murakami, Y. (2013), Affection Of Contact And Transcendental Telepathy from The Free Dictionary.com/Paranoia. Paranoid ideation. (nd) in Psychology dictionary retrieved from the Psychology dictionary

55. National Library Of Medicine   Literacy Among People with serious mental illness!

56. National Library Of Medicine (2013) The Psychosis Of High Risk State: A comprehensive State-Of-The-Art Review Jama Psychiatry pp.1 DOI 10.1001/jama psychiatry.2013.269

57. New Testament

58. Non- Bazaar delusion Cleveland Clinic

59. Oatman Jr., Johnson- Lyrics Gabriel Charles Hutchinson- Music   Higher Ground

60. Old Testament.

61. Paranoia   Mayo Clinic

62. Peale, N. The Power Of Positive Thinking Goalcast

63. Peale N. Brainy Quotes Google

64. Peale N. (A-Z) quotes Google

65. Philman, Regis "Weve All Been Delusion"

66. Post Hoc Ergo Proptor Hoc Fallacy-   Wikipedia

67. Pythagorus Google

68. Quest Bright Treatment Centers

69. Roberts Oral "Expect A Miracle"

70. Roberts Oral "Something Good Is Going To Happen To You"

71. Roosevelt, Franklin, Deleanor, "There is nothing to fear but fear itself" FDR's inaugural address 1933

aturn

72. Ruiz D. (1960) Epidemiology Of Schzophrenia; Some Diagnostic And Socicultural Considerations Phylon 43 (4), pp. 315-326 DOI: 10.2307/2754No 4 (4th quarter-1982), pp. 315-326

73. Saavedra, J., Lopez M. Gonzales S., Cubero R. Does Employment Promote Recovery? Meanings From Work Experience In People Diagnosed With Serious Mental Illness. M Cult Med Psychiatry, pp. 511DOI 10.1007/s 11013-015-9481-4

74. Sacks, M.H. Carpenter, W.T., Strauss, J.S., Bethesda, 1974, Recovery From Delusions, arch Gen Arch. Psychiatry/Vol 30, pp. 118

75. Sartre, Jean, Paul, Freedom and Self-creation, pg. 95, Self an World James A. Ogilvy

76. Sass, L., Byron, G. (2015), Self- Disturbance And The Bizrre: On Incomprehensibility In Schizophrenic Delusions Psychopathology, 48 pp. 293-300 DOI 101159/000437210 da

77. Sayadaw U. Siladaw pp. 18 Mindfulness And Clear Comprehension

aturn

78. Schafer I. and Fisher H., Childhood Trauma & psychosis- What is the evidence Scopophobia .(nd) in Free Dictionary retrieved Medical dictionary- The Free Dictionary.com/scopohbia,

79. Shakespeare "know thyself"

80. Schizophrenia, Schizophrenia Bulletin, 36, (1), DOI: 10.1093/schbulsbp144

81. Scopophobia Quoro

82. Seger, Bob, You'll Accompany Me

83. Shakespeare, W., Act II Scene VII Line 139, (1599), The Globe

84. Smith, M. and Segal, J (2017) Schizophrenia Symptoms, Signs, & Coping Tips, HELPGUIDE. ORG, PP. 1

85. Social Defeat The British Journal Of Psychiatry) vol.187) Issue(2) DOI https://sdg/ 10.1192/bip.187.2.101

86. Sociology Wikipedia

87. Startup M., Bucci S., Langdon, R.., (2009) Delusions Of Reference: A New Theoretical Model DOI 10.1080/13546800902864229

88. Stereotyping Of Race And Gender Wikipedia

aturn

89. Stevens, Ray Everything is Beautiful

90. Subliminal Persuasion Social Media Today

91. Subliminal Persuasion Free Dictionary

92. Subliminal Persuasion Wikipedia

93. Symbol-Wikipedia

94. Symbolism- Literary Devices

95. Symbolic Communication- Wikipedia

96. Symbolic Interactionism- Ashley Crossman

97. Symbolic Interactionism- Wikipedia

98. Szasz, Thomas Wikipedia

99. The Archies Honey, honey, sugar, sugar

100.   The Pointer Sisters The Heat Is On

101.   Trauma, Merrian Webster dictionary

102.   Waldfogel, J., Kelly, B., Garfunkel, I., Public Assistance Programs: How Much Could Be Saved With Improvd Eduation?

103.   (2005) Columbia University School Social Work

104.   Withers, Bill Lean on me

105.   ZZ.H. Li, Z., Nolanista, TN., Arthur D. Wang, H., HU,L (2013) Self-Management Education Interventions

aturn